THE AUSTRALIAN
Women's Weekly
low-fat diet

lose up to 5kgs in 21 days by following this simple diet

acp
books

CONTENTS

The oven temperatures in this book are for conventional ovens; if you have a fan-forced oven, decrease the oven temperature by 10–20 degrees. A measurement conversion chart appears on the back flap of this book.

STEPS TO SUCCESS

A healthy eating plan that is balanced, low-in-fat but high-in-taste: sound impossible? Well, it's not. Our key to success is a menu plan with less than 20g fat per day.

ATTACK THE FAT

The average Australian consumes between 50g to 60g each day. Fat is not our enemy, however, with obesity rates in Australia at an all-time high, it is important that we educate ourselves about fat, and recognise the difference between 'good' and 'bad' fats. We've all heard of saturated fats and trans fats: these are 'bad' fats. Found in fatty meats, deep-fried takeaway food and commercial cakes; 'bad' fats increase the risk of heart disease and contribute to high blood cholesterol. 'Good' fats, such as polyunsaturated fats and monounsaturated fats, are abundant in oils such as sunflower and olive, as well as salmon, tuna, nuts, lean meats and seeds – these fats can help lower blood cholesterol and reduce the risk of heart disease.

21 DAYS OF DISCIPLINE

True to Women's Weekly style, the recipes we've developed are easy-to-follow – there are no hard-to-find ingredients. We believe that it's imperative to eat in order to trim down; by eating three meals and two snacks per day, for 21 days, you'll find that you lose weight in a fashion that is good for your body.

FACTS ABOUT THIS DIET

This diet is based on the Healthy Eating Pyramid and follows the Australian Dietary Guidelines. It is a serious weight-loss diet that will supply your body with around 4000kJ (1000 cal) per day. The diet is for two people, and is based on three meals to be shared and two snacks per person, per day.

ARE YOU READY TO LOSE WEIGHT?

There's no point embarking on a lifestyle change unless you're mentally prepared. Without the commitment, the drive and the passion to achieve results for yourself with this diet, it will be a challenge to be successful. It's important that you're organised and prepared for this diet, so you don't give yourself a chance to slip back into bad habits.

SWAPPING DAYS

Feel free to swap days around on the diet to suit your lifestyle. For example, if you look at the menu for Day 6 and think that you would rather have the food from Day 11 instead, then just swap them around. Same goes for the snacks - feel free to chop and change. By making changes like this, you're making life easier for yourself, and you'll find it easier to stick to the diet.

EXERCISING

Did you know that if you eat a 50g (1½-ounce) piece of milk chocolate, you need to walk briskly for over 60 minutes to burn off the kilojoules? Whether you like it or not, exercise is integral to weight loss. Moderate exercise will help you lose weight and tone your body, but it makes you feel good, too.

WHAT TO DRINK

Drink at least 2 litres (8 cups) of water every day; include tea, coffee etc., in this count. Water aids with satiety (feeling full), and a glass of water is certainly better for you than a chocolate biscuit. By drinking lots of water, you're helping your skin, hair and eyes to look great. People who drink a lot of water generally have a clear complexion, shiny hair and a sparkle in their eyes.

We suggest you avoid alcohol-based drinks while you're on this diet. If you choose to have a glass of wine, drink it slowly. Alcohol, in particular beer, contains a lot of kilojoules so opt for a dry white wine or champagne. The best option however, is to drink water.

WEIGHTS AND MEASURES

The recipes in this diet have been carefully measured and triple-tested, so it is important to use the weights that we've given in the recipes, to ensure you are getting the nutrition we intended. Invest in kitchen scales if you don't own them already.

ADDING FLAVOUR

Flavour-enhancers like chilli, mustard, herbs and spices can be used with abandon as they contain a negligible amount of fat and kilojoules. Take care when using cooking-oil spray, as a 1-second spray of oil is measured as 1g of fat, so apply it sparingly.

WEIGH-IN

Weighing yourself every day will not give you a true reflection of your weight-loss; weight can fluctuate from day-to-day. Weigh yourself naked to give a true indication of what you weigh. It's good to weigh

yourself at the same time, for example, 7am every Monday morning; and make sure you use the same set of scales every time.

SLEEP WELL, LOOK SWELL

Keep your energy levels high and mood positive by getting at least eight hours sleep a night. A good night's sleep is also necessary to give your body time to repair; your body is constantly working, using the nutrients it collects from your food to strengthen and recharge your muscles.

STRATEGIC EATING

Holidays, birthday parties, work functions, dinner parties ... the list can go on and on – these are all events where over-eating is notorious. Being on a diet doesn't mean you have to avoid attending special occasions, you simply need to make smart eating choices, ensuring you don't fall of the diet wagon too much. If you're dining out, don't be shy to ask the waiter if you can alter the meal slightly to suit your dietary needs; for example, ask for grilled fish instead of fried or for sauces and dressings to be served on the side – it's all about strategic eating.

STRESS RELIEVERS

It makes a great deal of difference if you have a 'support team' by your side during the diet. Whether it's your partner, your next-door neighbour or a group of girls from work, a little bit of support goes a long way.

DEAR DIARY

Another easy way to keep yourself on track is to write a journal – doing so helps you remain accountable for your actions; like they say, if you cheat, you're only cheating yourself. Every day, jot down how you felt about the meals you ate and the exercise you did, record your weight loss and any thoughts you want to share with yourself. As the days go by, you can flick back and reflect on the progress you have made.

SHOPPING LISTS

The best way to tackle the supermarket is to write a shopping list – and stick to it. We've made sure there are no ingredients used in the diet plan that can't be found in a regular supermarket, and we've also supplied a list of food needed each week (see page 112) to make shopping even easier.

DON'T SHOP HUNGRY

Avoid shopping on an empty stomach; if you're hungry, you're more likely to be tempted to buy the foods that you shouldn't eat.

A+ FOR EFFORT

If you want to sustain your weight loss, you need to put in effort. After being disciplined for 21 days and achieving fantastic results, you don't want to undo all the hard work you've done; identify your vices, whether it's pizzas, chocolate bars or thick shakes, and steer clear of them.

MEET THE DIETERS

Our four dieters are tempted every day with lots of wonderful food as they create and develop recipes for our books. And, because we triple test all our recipes, these four are constantly in the kitchen, tweaking and tasting food. For our dieters to lose weight, the diet had to be easy to follow, and fit in alongside their family, job and social commitments.

PAMELA Our Food Director not only taste tests our recipes, but frequently attends social and family functions where there's a lot of tempting food on offer that is hard to refuse. Even with all these events, Pamela lost 3kg on this diet, and will continue it to lose some more.

EMMA Our Food Editor has a hungry husband, three ravenous kids and a busy family and social life. The meals had to be filling enough to feed the family, and lunches flexible enough to be eaten at soccer games on the weekend. While not on the diet, the family enjoyed the recipes, too. Emma lost 4.8kg.

CHARLOTTE As the youngest member of the team, our Food Assistant found that working in the Test Kitchen did have a down side... the weight she put on after starting to work with us. She was thrilled at how tasty and filling the meals were, and was over the moon to lose 5.5kg.

HIEU With a hectic social life, and friends eager to try new restaurants, our Creative Director needed to find time between planned events to keep to this diet. After finding it a little hard at first, he still managed to lose 6kg. It just goes to show that treating yourself occasionally isn't all bad.

DAY 1

high-fibre mixed berry yogurt smoothies

PREP TIME 5 MINUTES SERVES 2

1 cup (250ml) skim milk

¼ cup (25g) crushed Weet-Bix

⅓ cup (95g) low-fat berry yogurt

½ cup (75g) frozen mixed berries

1 Blend or process ingredients until smooth.

tips You can use ½ cup of fresh mixed berries and four ice-cubes instead of the frozen berries. Garnish with extra fresh berries, if you like. You need 1¼ Weet-Bix for the smoothie. Weet-Bix is a wheat-based breakfast cereal biscuit containing oven-roasted whole wheat grains, sugar, salt and barley malt extract.

DIARY ENTRY

This morning I woke up early and took the dog for a 50-minute walk. The smoothie was a delicious way to get the day off to a healthy start. The mid-morning snack of corn thins and avocado, which was scrumptious, got me through to lunch. It is amazing: eating at regular intervals throughout the day really keeps your energy up. Dinner was delicious, very filling; when I make this again, I would replace the preserved lemon rind with some fresh lemon zest and juice."
– Emma

Just the thought of going on a diet makes me hungry already. First up, we started with a smoothie; I could have had 4 of them along with my usual bacon and egg sandwich. On the plus side, it was delicious. Lunch and dinner were smaller portions than what I'm used to. With snacks, which I normally never have, I wasn't as hungry as I thought.
– Hieu

nutritional count per 1 cup (250ml) serving
▶ 1g total fat
▶ 0.4g saturated fat
▶ 830kJ (198 cal)
▶ 30.9g carbohydrate
▶ 14.9g protein
▶ 2.9g fibre

chicken and cucumber pittas

PREP + COOK TIME 25 MINUTES SERVES 2

cooking-oil spray

150g (4½-ounce) chicken breast fillet

1 lebanese cucumber (130g)

2 teaspoons white wine vinegar

1 teaspoon white (granulated) sugar

1 small fresh red thai chilli (serrano), chopped finely

¼ cup loosely packed fresh coriander leaves (cilantro)

¼ cup loosely packed fresh mint leaves

½ teaspoon light soy sauce

2 pocket pitta breads (70g)

½ small butter lettuce

1 medium lemon (140g)

1 Lightly spray heated grill plate (or grill or barbecue); cook chicken until browned both sides and cooked through, cool. Use forks to shred chicken.

2 Meanwhile, slice cucumber into long, thin strips with a vegetable peeler. Combine cucumber, vinegar, sugar, chilli, coriander, mint and sauce in medium bowl; stand 10 minutes.

3 Fill pittas equally with chicken, pickled cucumber and lettuce; season. Serve with a squeeze of lemon.

note Freeze leftover pitta breads to use in later recipes.

nutritional count per serving
▶ 5.2g total fat
▶ 1.5g saturated fat
▶ 961kJ (226 cal)
▶ 25.4g carbohydrate
▶ 20.4g protein
▶ 4.6g fibre

spiced-rubbed beef with chickpea salad

PREP + COOK TIME 45 MINUTES (+ REFRIGERATION) **SERVES** 2

½ teaspoon coriander seeds

½ teaspoon dried chilli flakes

½ teaspoon sea salt

1 clove garlic, crushed

300g (9½-ounce) piece beef eye fillet, trimmed

3 large egg (plum) tomatoes (270g), peeled

250g (8 ounces) canned chickpeas, rinsed, drained

1 tablespoon finely chopped preserved lemon rind

½ cup finely chopped fresh flat-leaf parsley

½ cup loosely packed fresh coriander leaves

2 teaspoons lemon juice

cooking-oil spray

100g (3 ounces) baby spinach leaves

1 Using mortar and pestle, crush seeds, chilli, salt and garlic into a coarse paste; rub paste onto beef. Cover; refrigerate 20 minutes.

2 Preheat oven to 200°C/400°F. Line oven tray with baking paper.

3 Meanwhile, quarter tomatoes; discard seeds and pulp. Chop tomato flesh finely. Place in medium bowl with chickpeas, rind, herbs and juice; toss gently to combine.

4 Lightly spray heated grill plate (or grill or barbecue); cook beef until browned all over. Transfer to oven tray; cook, uncovered, in oven, 20 minutes (for medium) or until cooked as you like.

5 Cover beef; stand 10 minutes, then slice thinly. Serve with salad; accompany with spinach.

note We used 2 x 125g (4-ounce) cans of chickpeas in this recipe.

nutritional count per serving
▶ 11.5g total fat
▶ 3.8g saturated fat
▶ 1382kJ (330 cal)
▶ 12.3g carbohydrate
▶ 40.3g protein
▶ 7.6g fibre

DAY 2

sautéed mushrooms on toast

PREP + COOK TIME 25 MINUTES **SERVES** 2

cooking-oil spray

100g (3 ounces) swiss brown mushrooms, sliced thickly

150g (4½ ounces) small button mushrooms

50g (1½ ounces) oyster mushrooms, halved

1 clove garlic, crushed

2 tablespoons water

4 slices ciabatta bread (110g)

2 tablespoons fresh flat-leaf parsley leaves

2 tablespoons coarsely chopped fresh chives

1 Lightly spray heated large non-stick frying pan over medium heat; cook mushrooms and garlic, stirring, about 5 minutes. Add water; bring to the boil. Reduce heat; simmer, uncovered, about 5 minutes or until water evaporates and mushrooms have softened. Season.

2 Meanwhile, toast bread.

3 Stir herbs into mushrooms; serve on toast.

note Freeze leftover ciabatta bread to use in later recipes.

DIARY ENTRY

When I was younger I thought it was a myth that it was harder to lose weight when you're older – I now know it's not, but I'm determined to stick to the diet – with only a little recipe tasting on the horizon over the next three weeks. The food yesterday was yummy and I didn't feel hungry until this afternoon – now I can barely wait to eat my chicken with barley tonight – barley is such a good grain.
– Pamela

Are the meals getting smaller and smaller? My stomach is starting to make weird noises. Very hungry all afternoon. Dinner wasn't bad and the portion was sufficient. Not full, but not starving either. Cycled for one hour after work.
– Hieu

nutritional count per serving
▶ 3.2g total fat
▶ 0.4g saturated fat
▶ 859kJ (205 cal)
▶ 28.9g carbohydrate
▶ 11.8g protein
▶ 5.9g fibre

tuna salad

PREP TIME 5 MINUTES **SERVES** 2

250g (8 ounces) tuna slices in lemon pepper, drained

100g (3 ounces) baby spinach leaves

3 teaspoons baby capers, rinsed, drained

125g (4 ounces) cherry tomatoes, halved

1 tablespoon fresh dill

2 tablespoons lemon juice

2 teaspoons olive oil

1 Combine tuna, spinach, capers, tomato and dill in large bowl.
2 Combine juice and oil in screw-top jar; shake well.
3 Pour lemon mixture over salad; toss to combine.

tip We used 2 x 125g (4-ounce) cans sliced tuna in this recipe.

nutritional count per serving
▶ 6.6g total fat   ▶ 6.4g carbohydrate
▶ 1.2g saturated fat ▶ 19.1g protein
▶ 714kJ (170 cal)   ▶ 3g fibre

grilled chicken with barley pilaf

PREP + COOK TIME 1 HOUR SERVES 2

½ cup (100g) pearl barley

1 cup (250ml) water

1 cup (250ml) chicken stock

200g (4 ounces) mixed tomato medley

cooking-oil spray

2 x 150g (4½-ounce) chicken breast fillets

½ cup coarsely chopped fresh flat-leaf parsley

1 green onion (scallion), sliced thinly

½ cup fresh basil leaves

2 teaspoons dijon mustard

1 Preheat oven to 220°C/475°F. Line oven tray with baking paper.

2 Cook barley with the water and stock in medium saucepan, uncovered, over low heat, about 50 minutes or until most of the liquid is absorbed, stirring occasionally.

3 Meanwhile, place tomatoes on oven tray; roast, uncovered, 15 minutes or until just softened.

4 Lightly spray heated grill plate (or grill or barbecue); cook chicken until browned both sides and cooked through.

5 Gently stir parsley, onion and half the basil into barley; season. Combine tomatoes with remaining basil. Dollop chicken with mustard; serve with pilaf and tomato mixture.

nutritional count per serving
- 10.2g total fat
- 3g saturated fat
- 1709kJ (402 cal)
- 34.4g carbohydrate
- 39.4g protein
- 9.5g fibre

DAY 3

low-fat toasted muesli

PREP + COOK TIME 40 MINUTES **MAKES** 5½ CUPS

⅔ cup (60g) rolled oats

⅓ cup (30g) triticale flakes

⅓ cup (20g) unprocessed bran

½ cup (65g) barley flakes

½ cup (25g) spelt flakes

½ cup (30g) rice flakes

1 tablespoon olive oil

2 tablespoons honey

2 tablespoons pepitas (pumpkin seeds)

1 tablespoon linseeds

1 tablespoon sunflower seed kernels

⅓ cup (50g) coarsely chopped dried apricots

⅓ cup (20g) coarsely chopped dried apples

⅓ cup (45g) coarsely chopped seeded dried dates

⅓ cup (55g) sultanas

⅔ cup (160ml) skim milk

1 Preheat oven to 180°C/350°F.

2 Combine cereals, oil and honey in large shallow baking dish. Toast, uncovered, about 20 minutes or until browned lightly, stirring at least three times during cooking time.

3 Cool cereal; stir in remaining dry ingredients.

4 Serve ½ cup muesli with ⅓ milk.

note Store in an airtight container in the refrigerator for up to 3 months.

serving suggestion Serve with fresh stone fruit or berries.

DIARY ENTRY

Not as hungry as day 2, and the muesli breakfast was delicious. I would make this recipe again on a regular basis.
- Hieu

nutritional count per ½ cup (60g) serving (with milk)

▶ 5.3g total fat

▶ 0.8g saturated fat

▶ 813kJ (194 cal)

▶ 30.1g carbohydrate

▶ 5.5g protein

▶ 4.1g fibre

vegetable and red lentil soup

PREP + COOK TIME 30 MINUTES **SERVES** 2

1 tablespoon curry paste

400g (12½ ounces) canned diced tomatoes

1½ cups (375ml) chicken stock

1 small carrot (70g), chopped finely

1 stalk celery (150g), trimmed, chopped finely

1 small potato (120g), chopped finely

1 small zucchini (90g), chopped finely

⅓ cup (65g) dried red lentils

¼ cup (30g) frozen peas

2 tablespoons low-fat plain yogurt

2 tablespoons coarsely chopped fresh coriander leaves (cilantro)

1 Cook curry paste in heated large saucepan, stirring, about one minute or until fragrant. Add undrained tomatoes, stock, carrot, celery, potato and zucchini; bring to the boil. Reduce heat; simmer, covered, 5 minutes.

2 Add lentils to soup mixture; return to the boil. Reduce heat; simmer, uncovered, about 10 minutes or until lentils are just tender. Add peas; return to the boil. Reduce heat; simmer, uncovered, until peas are just tender.

3 Remove soup from heat; stir in yogurt and coriander.

note While a hot curry paste, or some finely chopped chilli, will boost the flavour, you can use any curry paste you like.

---

nutritional count per serving

▶ 5.8g total fat
▶ 0.9g saturated fat
▶ 1180kJ (282 cal)
▶ 34.7g carbohydrate
▶ 16.7g protein
▶ 12.6g fibre

nutritional count per serving
▶ 6.4g total fat
▶ 1.6g saturated fat
▶ 1592kJ (380 cal)
▶ 26.7g carbohydrate
▶ 48.7g protein
▶ 6.9g fibre

asian-style fish cakes with cucumber and carrot salad

PREP + COOK TIME 25 MINUTES SERVES 2

cooking-oil spray

400g (12½ ounces) firm white fish fillets

1 large potato (300g), chopped coarsely

1 green onion (scallions), sliced thinly

1 clove garlic, crushed

2cm (¾-inch) piece fresh ginger (10g), grated

1 small fresh thai red chilli (serrano), chopped finely

1 egg white, lightly beaten

CUCUMBER AND CARROT SALAD

1 lebanese cucumber (130g)

1 medium carrot (120g)

50g (1½ ounces) snow peas, trimmed

½ cup loosely packed fresh coriander leaves (cilantro)

25g (¾ ounce) snow pea sprouts, trimmed

¼ cup (60ml) lime juice

1 small fresh thai red chilli (serrano), chopped finely

1 Lightly spray heated large non-stick frying pan over medium heat; cook fish about 3 minutes each side or until just cooked. Flake with a fork.

2 Boil, steam or microwave potato until tender; drain. Mash potato in large bowl. Add fish; mash with fork until well combined. Stir in onion, garlic, ginger, chilli and egg white until well combined.

3 Using wet hands, shape mixture into 6 even-sized patties, refrigerate 10 minutes.

4 Meanwhile, make cucumber and carrot salad.

5 Cook patties, in batches, in same heated large frying pan over medium heat until browned both sides and heated through.

6 Serve fish cakes with salad, and a squeeze of lime, if you like.

CUCUMBER AND CARROT SALAD Using a vegetable peeler, cut cucumber and carrot into thin ribbons. Combine cucumber, carrot, snow peas, coriander and sprouts in medium bowl. Pour over combined juice and chilli; toss to combine.

tips Fish cakes can be made ahead; store, covered, in the refrigerator. If you find the patties are too soft, use an egg ring to help them hold their shape while cooking.

DAY 4

minted fruit salad

PREP + COOK TIME 35 MINUTES (+ REFRIGERATION) SERVES 2

¾ cup (180ml) water

2 teaspoons grated palm sugar

1 star anise

1 tablespoon lime juice

½ small pineapple (400g), peeled, chopped coarsely

½ small honeydew melon (450g), peeled, chopped coarsely

250g (8 ounces) fresh lychees, peeled, seeded

100g (3 ounces) seedless red grapes, halved

¼ cup loosely packed fresh mint leaves

1 Stir the water, sugar and star anise in small saucepan over medium heat until sugar dissolves. Simmer, uncovered, 10 minutes. Stir in juice. Cover; refrigerate 3 hours. Strain syrup into medium jug; discard star anise.
2 Combine fruit, mint and syrup in large bowl.

notes Make syrup the night before. If you can't buy the fruits, due to seasonal availability, you can substitute with a mixture of fruits such as watermelon, kiwi fruit, blueberries and strawberries; just make sure you have the same total weight of fruit. You could also use canned lychees if fresh ones aren't in season.

DIARY ENTRY

This week is the kids' cakes photoshoot, so I have been completely surrounded by lollies and chocolates. Today I succumbed and ate a whole chocolate bar... I feel so guilty! But I can't let it discourage me. Back to the diet with the tasty smoked chicken sandwich and the pork with beetroot salad for dinner. I really loved the beetroot salad with the goat's cheese — I am going to add that salad to my regulars.
- Charlotte

I prepared today's breakfast last night while organising meals for my family. While cooking tonight's dinner I prepared the ingredients for tomorrow's breakfast, and the pea and ricotta mixture for tomorrow's lunch. I find preparing meals the evening before makes sticking to the diet easy, and I don't need to fuss when I'm busy.
- Emma

nutritional count per serving

▶ 0.7g total fat
▶ 0.1g saturated fat
▶ 742kJ (177 cal)
▶ 36.1g carbohydrate
▶ 3.2g protein
▶ 6.4g fibre

smoked chicken open sandwiches

PREP + COOK TIME 10 MINUTES SERVES 2

4 slices ciabatta bread (110g)

2 teaspoons reduced-fat mayonnaise

200g (6½ ounces) thinly sliced smoked chicken

20g (¾ ounce) mixed salad leaves

2 tablespoons mango chutney

1 Toast bread.

2 Spread mayonnaise over toasts; top with chicken, salad leaves and chutney.

note Use the ciabatta bread that was left over from day 2.

nutritional count per serving

▶ 9g total fat

▶ 2.3g saturated fat

▶ 1523kJ (364 cal)

▶ 38.7g carbohydrate

▶ 31.1g protein

▶ 2.2g fibre

pork steaks with beetroot salad

PREP + COOK TIME 1¼ HOURS SERVES 2

200g (6½ ounces) fresh beetroot

2 teaspoons caraway seeds

1 teaspoon olive oil

2 x 150g (4½-ounce) boneless pork steaks

cooking-oil spray

75g (2½ ounces) firm goat's cheese, crumbled

3 large red radishes (105g), sliced thinly

125g (4 ounces) baby rocket leaves (arugula)

DIJON VINAIGRETTE

1 teaspoon dijon mustard

1 teaspoon olive oil

1 tablespoon red wine vinegar

1 Preheat oven to 200°C/400°F.

2 Discard beetroot stems and leaves; place unpeeled beetroot in small shallow baking dish. Roast, uncovered, about 45 minutes or until beetroot is tender. Cool 10 minutes; peel beetroot, then cut into wedges.

3 Meanwhile, make dijon vinaigrette.

4 Using mortar and pestle, crush seeds and oil into a paste; rub into pork. Lightly spray heated grill plate (or grill or barbecue); cook pork until browned both sides and cooked as desired.

5 Place beetroot, cheese, radish and rocket in large bowl with vinaigrette; toss gently to combine. Serve salad with pork.

DIJON VINAIGRETTE Combine ingredients in screw-top jar; shake well.

tip To save time you could use 200g (6½ ounces) drained canned baby beetroot.

nutritional count per serving	
▶ 13.5g total fat	▶ 11g carbohydrate
▶ 5.2g saturated fat	▶ 43.3g protein
▶ 1458kJ (348 cal)	▶ 4.5g fibre

DAY 5

spinach omelettes

PREP + COOK TIME 30 MINUTES SERVES 2

250g (8 ounces) baby truss egg (plum) tomatoes

250g (8 ounces) baby spinach leaves

1 small brown onion (80g), sliced thinly

1 tablespoon water

4 egg whites

2 tablespoons skim milk

cooking-oil spray

1 Preheat oven to 220°C/425°F.
2 Place tomatoes on oven tray. Roast about 10 minutes or until tomatoes are just softened.
3 Rinse spinach briefly under cold water; shake until almost dry. Cook spinach, in batches, in 20cm (8-inch) (base measurement) non-stick frying pan, over medium heat, until just starting to wilt. Place in medium bowl; cool.

4 Reheat same pan; cook onion and the water, uncovered, over medium heat, stirring occasionally, until onion is soft. Combine onion with the spinach in bowl. Wipe pan clean.
5 Meanwhile, using a fork, beat 2 egg whites with 1 tablespoon milk in small bowl until combined.
6 Lightly spray same heated pan. Pour egg-white mixture into pan; cook, over low heat, until just browned underneath. Place pan under hot grill; cook until top just sets.
7 Sprinkle half the spinach mixture over one half of the omelette; grill until mixture is hot and top is browned lightly. Fold omelette in half to enclose filling. Cover to keep warm.
8 Repeat to make another omelette; serve omelettes with tomatoes.

notes The frying pan goes under the grill in this recipe, so you need a frying pan with an ovenproof handle, or cover the handle with a few layers of foil to protect it from the heat of the grill. If you don't have a lid for the frying pan, cover it with foil. Cook the recipe just before serving.

DIARY ENTRY

Last night a lean, but flavoursome pork chop was on the menu for dinner and, even though the accompaniment was a salad, the main ingredient was beetroot – I really love beetroot. I'm feeling slightly lighter, and leaner, each day.
- Pamela

Had a 3-day holiday booked, so I will be going off the diet. Weighed myself on the morning of Day 5 – had lost 4kgs.
- Hieu

nutritional count per serving
▶ 0.6g total fat
▶ 0g saturated fat
▶ 404kJ (97 cal)
▶ 7.1g carbohydrate
▶ 12.6g protein
▶ 5.3g fibre

pea, ricotta, mint and spinach open sandwiches

PREP + COOK TIME 10 MINUTES SERVES 2

½ cup (60g) frozen peas

100g (3 ounces) low-fat ricotta cheese

2 teaspoons finely grated lemon rind

1 tablespoon lemon juice

2 tablespoons finely chopped mint

4 slices soy and linseed bread (180g)

40g (1 ounce) baby spinach leaves

1 Boil, steam or microwave peas until tender; drain, cool. Using fork, lightly crush peas.
2 Combine peas in small bowl with ricotta, rind, juice and mint.
3 Toast bread. Sandwich spinach and pea mixture between toast slices.

nutritional count per serving
- ▶ 12.9g total fat
- ▶ 3.9g saturated fat
- ▶ 1482kJ (354 cal)
- ▶ 35.5g carbohydrate
- ▶ 19.1g protein
- ▶ 8.6g fibre

prawns with fennel salad

PREP + COOK TIME 35 MINUTES SERVES 2

16 uncooked large king prawns (1.1kg)

1 teaspoon ground fennel

1 tablespoon white wine vinegar

1 clove garlic, crushed

1 teaspoon olive oil

1 baby cos lettuce (200g)

1 small fennel bulb (200g), sliced thinly

½ cup firmly packed fresh flat-leaf parsley leaves

MUSTARD DRESSING

1½ tablespoons white wine vinegar

¼ teaspoon dijon mustard

2 teaspoons olive oil

½ teaspoon white (granulated) sugar

2 green onions (scallions), chopped coarsely

1 Shell and devein prawns, leaving tails intact.

2 Combine prawns in medium bowl with ground fennel, vinegar, garlic and oil; toss gently. Season.

3 Make mustard dressing.

4 Cook prawns on heated grill plate (or grill or barbecue) about 4 minutes or until changed in colour and cooked through.

5 Meanwhile, divide lettuce leaves between serving plates; top with fennel and parsley. Drizzle with dressing. Serve prawns on salad.

MUSTARD DRESSING Combine ingredients in screw-top jar; shake well, season to taste.

note Use either red or green cos lettuce.

nutritional count per serving

▶ 8.8g total fat
▶ 1.2g saturated fat
▶ 1447kJ (346 cal)
▶ 4.3g carbohydrate
▶ 58.6g protein
▶ 4.3g fibre

DAY 6

eggs ranchero-style

PREP + COOK TIME 25 MINUTES SERVES 2

cooking-oil spray

½ small red onion (50g), chopped finely

2 medium tomatoes (300g), chopped coarsely

1 tablespoon water

2 teaspoons balsamic vinegar

1 small red capsicum (bell pepper) (150g), chopped finely

2 small corn tortillas

2 eggs

¼ cup fresh coriander (cilantro) leaves

1 Lightly spray heated large non-stick frying pan; cook onion, stirring, over medium heat, until onion is softened. Add tomato, the water and vinegar; bring to the boil. Reduce heat; simmer, covered, 5 minutes, stirring occasionally. Add capsicum; cook, uncovered, 5 minutes.

2 Meanwhile, warm tortillas according to packet directions.

3 Using large shallow mixing spoon, press two shallow depressions into tomato mixture. Working quickly, break eggs, one at a time, into cup, sliding each egg into one of the hollows in the tomato mixture. Cover pan; cook over low heat, about 5 minutes or until eggs are just set.

4 Divide warmed tortillas among plates. Use egg slide to carefully lift egg and tomato mixture onto each tortilla; top with coriander to serve.

DIARY ENTRY

I didn't think I would feel up to making the eggs for breakfast, but it wasn't hard, and turned out to be really yummy. It set me up for a lazy day pottering about at home.
– Charlotte

I always find it hard to eat properly on weekends when I'm running about with the kids, taking them to and from sport. For breakfast I had a bowl of the muesli left over from day 3, and I packed the ham, avocado and roasted tomato sandwiches to take to soccer. Knowing that I had lunch packed, made it easier to resist the usual Saturday sausage sandwich.
– Emma

nutritional count per serving
▶ 3.3g total fat
▶ 0.9g saturated fat
▶ 457kJ (109 cal)
▶ 10.6g carbohydrate
▶ 7.1g protein
▶ 3.6g fibre

ham, tomato and avocado open sandwiches

PREP + COOK TIME 20 MINUTES SERVES 2

2 medium egg (plum) tomatoes (150g), halved

1 tablespoon light brown sugar

4 slices ciabatta bread (140g)

½ small avocado (100g), sliced

100g (3 ounces) shaved ham

1 Preheat oven to 200°C/400°F.

2 Place tomato, cut-side up, on oven tray, sprinkle with sugar; roast, uncovered, 15 minutes.

3 Toast bread; top toasts with avocado, ham and tomato. Season.

tips Tomatoes can be roasted a day ahead. Cover, refrigerate.
Use ciabatta that was left over from day 2.

nutritional count per serving
▶ 14.7g total fat
▶ 3.3g saturated fat
▶ 1599kJ (382 cal)
▶ 41.6g carbohydrate
▶ 19g protein
▶ 3.7g fibre

lamb and lentil curry

PREP + COOK TIME 35 MINUTES SERVES 2

½ cup (100g) yellow split peas

cooking-oil spray

300g (9½ ounces) lamb fillets, cut into 4cm pieces

1 large brown onion (200g), sliced thinly

2cm (¾-inch) piece fresh ginger (10g), chopped finely

1 clove garlic, crushed

1 tablespoon ground coriander

1 teaspoon hot paprika

¼ teaspoon cayenne pepper

1 medium tomato (150g), chopped coarsely

⅓ cup (80ml) light coconut cream

¾ cup (180ml) chicken stock

75g (2½ ounces) baby spinach leaves

6 mini pappadums (20g)

¼ cup coarsely chopped fresh coriander (cilantro)

2 tablespoons low-fat plain yogurt

1 Place split peas in medium saucepan, cover with water; bring to the boil. Reduce heat, simmer, uncovered, about 30 minutes or until tender; drain.

2 Meanwhile, lightly spray large frying pan; cook lamb, stirring, over medium heat, until cooked as desired. Drain on absorbent paper.

3 Cook onion in same heated pan, stirring, about 5 minutes or until softened. Add ginger, garlic, ground coriander, paprika and cayenne; cook, stirring, until fragrant.

4 Add tomato, coconut cream and stock to pan; bring to the boil. Reduce heat; simmer, covered, about 5 minutes or until sauce thickens slightly.

5 Return lamb to pan with split peas and spinach; cook, stirring, until heated through.

6 Cook pappadums according to packet directions; serve with curry, fresh coriander and yogurt.

nutritional count per serving
- 18.7g total fat
- 7.5g saturated fat
- 2397kJ (573 cal)
- 33.9g carbohydrate
- 62.3g protein
- 11.6g fibre

DAY 7

corn fritters with tomato chutney

PREP + COOK TIME 40 MINUTES **SERVES** 2 (MAKES 18)

½ cup (80g) wholemeal self-raising flour

¼ teaspoon bicarbonate of soda

¼ teaspoon hot paprika

¼ cup (60ml) skim milk

1 egg, beaten lightly

1 cup (160g) fresh corn kernels

½ small red capsicum (bell pepper) (75g), chopped finely

1 green onion (scallion), sliced thinly

1 tablespoon finely chopped fresh flat-leaf parsley

cooking-oil spray

¼ cup (80g) tomato chutney

100g (3 ounces) watercress

1 Sift flour, soda and paprika into medium bowl. Make well in centre; gradually stir in combined milk and egg until batter is smooth. Stir corn, capsicum, onion and parsley into batter.

2 Spoon 1 tablespoon of batter into heated, lightly sprayed, large non-stick frying pan; using a spatula, spread batter into a round shape. Cook fritter, over low heat, about 2 minutes each side or until fritter is browned lightly and cooked through.

3 Remove from pan; cover to keep warm. Repeat with remaining batter. Serve fritters with chutney and watercress.

tips You need 1 medium fresh corn cob, weighing about 125g (4 ounces) after being trimmed. You can cook more than 1 fritter at a time, but don't overcrowd the pan.

DIARY ENTRY

The corn fritters was the tastiest brekkie I've had in a long time, and it was guilt free. I had people over for Sunday lunch, so I made a huge batch of the sang choy bow – everyone loved it and asked for the recipe. The mussels for dinner felt very indulgent, it's nice to feel indulgent on a diet for a change.
– Charlotte

Being a cold winter's morning it was nice to start the day with a warm breakfast, the tomato chilli jam had a really warming heat, which was delicious. I can't believe week one is over, I haven't felt like I've been dieting, all the food has been filling and delicious, and the program is easy to follow.
– Emma

sang choy bow

PREP + COOK TIME 25 MINUTES **SERVES** 2

1 teaspoon sesame oil

1 small brown onion (80g), chopped finely

1 clove garlic, crushed

300g (9½ ounces) minced (ground) pork and veal mixture

1½ tablespoons light soy sauce

1½ tablespoons oyster sauce

1 small red capsicum (bell pepper) (150g), chopped finely

1½ cups (120g) bean sprouts

2 green onions (scallions), chopped coarsely

4 large iceberg lettuce leaves

2 teaspoons toasted sesame seeds

1 Heat oil in wok; stir-fry brown onion and garlic, over medium heat, until onion softens. Add mince; stir-fry until cooked through. Add sauces and capsicum; reduce heat, simmer, uncovered, stirring occasionally, 3 minutes.

2 Just before serving, stir sprouts and green onion into mixture. Divide sang choy bow into lettuce leaves; sprinkle with sesame seeds to serve.

notes Some butchers sell a pork and veal mixture, however, if it is not available as a mixture, buy half the amount of pork mince and half the amount of veal mince.
Tap stem end of a cored iceberg lettuce soundly against the edge of your kitchen sink then hold the lettuce under cold running water; the leaves will fall off, one by one, intact.

nutritional count per serving
▶ 14.8g total fat
▶ 4.6g saturated fat
▶ 1388kJ (331 cal)
▶ 10.4g carbohydrate
▶ 37.1g protein
▶ 3.4g fibre

mussels with basil and lemon grass

PREP + COOK TIME 35 MINUTES SERVES 2

1kg (2 pounds) large black mussels

2 teaspoons olive oil

1 small brown onion (80g), chopped finely

2 cloves garlic, crushed

10cm (4-inch) stick fresh lemon grass (20g), sliced thinly

1 fresh long red chilli, chopped finely

1 cup (250ml) fish stock

2 tablespoons lime juice

2 tablespoons fish sauce

⅓ cup loosely packed fresh thai basil leaves

½ cup (125ml) light coconut milk

2 green onions (scallions), sliced thinly

1 Scrub mussels under cold water; remove beards.

2 Heat oil in wok; stir-fry brown onion, garlic, lemon grass and half the chilli, over medium heat, until onion softens and mixture is fragrant.

3 Add stock, juice and sauce; bring to the boil. Add mussels to pan; reduce heat, simmer, covered, about 5 minutes or until mussels open.

4 Meanwhile, shred basil finely. Add basil, coconut milk and green onion to wok; stir-fry until heated through. Place mussel mixture in serving bowl; sprinkle with remaining chilli. Serve with a squeeze of lime, if you like.

notes You will get about eight mussels per serve. Mussels should be bought from a fish market where there is reliably fresh fish. They must be tightly closed when bought, indicating they are alive. Some mussels might not open after cooking. These might need help with a knife or might not have cooked as quickly as the others. Pot-ready mussels come in 1kg bags. They have been scrubbed and bearded and are ready to cook. You can use these, if you like.

nutritional count per serving
▶ 6.7g total fat
▶ 1.2g saturated fat
▶ 1088kJ (260 cal)
▶ 12.6g carbohydrate
▶ 15.5g protein
▶ 2.2g fibre

DAY 8

watermelon and berry salad

PREP TIME 5 MINUTES **SERVES** 2

1kg (2-pound) piece seedless watermelon, chopped coarsely

250g (8 ounces) strawberries, halved

125g (4 ounces) blueberries

¼ cup loosely packed fresh mint leaves

1 Combine watermelon, berries and mint in medium bowl.

DIARY ENTRY

What a lovely start to Monday morning and week 2 of my 21-day journey – the scales have commended my efforts showing a loss of 2kg; so excited about the loss.
– Emma

Start of week 2. After a 3-day binge of food and wine, I was looking forward to restarting the diet. The fruit for breakfast was refreshing, after all the rich food that I had on the weekend. Gained 3kgs as a result of the weekend. Cycled for 40 minutes after work.
– Hieu

nutritional count per serving
▶ 0.9g total fat
▶ 0g saturated fat
▶ 597kJ (143 cal)
▶ 26.7g carbohydrate
▶ 3.6g protein
▶ 6.2g fibre

roast beef and horseradish cream wraps

PREP TIME 5 MINUTES SERVES 2

½ cup (120g) char-grilled capsicum (bell pepper)

2 teaspoons horseradish cream

2 rye mountain bread wraps (60g)

150g (4½ ounces) sliced rare roast beef

50g (1½ ounces) baby rocket leaves (arugula)

1 Drain capsicum well; pat dry with absorbent paper towel.
2 Spread horseradish over each wrap.
3 Divide beef, capsicum and rocket between wraps. Roll to enclose filling.

nutritional count per serving
- ▶ 7.5g total fat
- ▶ 1.7g saturated fat
- ▶ 889kJ (212 cal)
- ▶ 19g carbohydrate
- ▶ 18.6g protein
- ▶ 2.6g fibre

sumac and sesame-grilled fish with fattoush

PREP + COOK TIME 40 MINUTES SERVES 2

2 x 200g (6½-ounce) blue-eye cutlets

2 teaspoons sesame seeds

1 teaspoon dried chilli flakes

2 teaspoons sumac

1 teaspoon sea salt flakes

cooking-oil spray

1 medium lemon (140g), cut into wedges

FATTOUSH

2 pocket pitta breads (70g)

125g (4 ounces) red grape tomatoes, halved

125g (4 ounces) yellow teardrop tomatoes, halved

1 small green capsicum (150g), chopped coarsely

1 lebanese cucumber (130g), chopped coarsely

2 red radishes (70g), sliced thinly

2 green onions (scallions), sliced thinly

¾ cup firmly packed fresh flat-leaf parsley leaves

¼ cup coarsely chopped fresh mint

1 teaspoon olive oil

2 teaspoons lemon juice

1 clove garlic, crushed

1 Preheat grill (broiler). Make fattoush.

2 Combine fish, seeds, chilli, sumac and salt in large bowl.

3 Lightly spray heated grill plate (or grill or barbecue); cook fish mixture until cooked as desired. Serve fish with lemon and fattoush.

FATTOUSH Tear bread into small pieces; place on oven tray, toast under grill until browned lightly. Place bread in large bowl with tomato, capsicum, cucumber, radish, onion and herbs. Add combined oil, juice and garlic; toss gently to combine.

nutritional count per serving

▶ 10.6g total fat   ▶ 40.6g carbohydrate
▶ 2.2g saturated fat   ▶ 48.7g protein
▶ 2003kJ (478 cal)   ▶ 10.4g fibre

DAY 9

egg-white omelettes with mushrooms

PREP + COOK TIME 25 MINUTES **SERVES** 2

100g (3 ounces) sliced ham off the bone

cooking-oil spray

100g (3 ounces) button mushrooms, sliced thinly

6 egg whites

2 tablespoons finely chopped fresh chives

1 medium tomato (190g), chopped coarsely

¼ cup (30g) coarsely grated low-fat cheddar cheese

2 slices wholemeal bread (90g)

1 Trim and discard any fat from ham; cut into thin strips. Lightly spray 20cm (8-inch) (base measurement) non-stick frying pan; cook ham, stirring, over medium heat, until browned lightly; remove from pan. Cover to keep warm.

2 Cook mushrooms in same heated pan, stirring, until browned lightly. Remove from pan; add to ham, cover to keep warm. Wipe pan clean.

3 Meanwhile, beat three of the egg whites in small bowl with electric mixer until soft peaks form; fold in half the chives.

4 Preheat grill (broiler).

5 Pour egg-white mixture into same heated lightly sprayed frying pan; cook, uncovered, over low heat, about 2 minutes or until just browned underneath. sprinkle half the tomato over one half of the omelette. Top tomato with half the cheese. Place pan under hot grill; cook until top just sets and cheese melts. Top tomato with half the ham and mushroom; fold omelette in half to enclose filling. Carefully transfer omelette to serving plate; cover to keep warm. Repeat to make another omelette.

6 Toast bread. Serve omelettes with toast, garnish with extra chives, if you like.

notes Cook recipe just before serving. The frying pan goes under the grill in this recipe, so you need a frying pan with an ovenproof handle, or cover the handle with a few layers of foil to protect it from the heat of the grill.

DIARY ENTRY

I nervously weighed myself this morning and I've lost 2.5 kgs – I can't believe it! I have not been this light in many years. As a result of my enthusiasm, I have been telling everyone they MUST try this diet when it comes out, it really works!
- Charlotte

nutritional count per serving
- ▶ 4.5g total fat
- ▶ 1.4g saturated fat
- ▶ 1120kJ (267 cal)
- ▶ 21.3g carbohydrate
- ▶ 32g protein
- ▶ 5.5g fibre

chilli beans

PREP + COOK TIME 30 MINUTES SERVES 2

1 teaspoon olive oil

1 small brown onion (80g), chopped coarsely

1 fresh long red chilli, sliced thinly

1 clove garlic, crushed

1 tablespoon tomato paste

400g (12½ ounces) canned diced tomatoes

2 tablespoons tomato sauce

2 teaspoons worcestershire sauce

420g (13½ ounces) canned cannellini beans, rinsed, drained

1 tablespoon coarsely chopped fresh flat-leaf parsley

1 tablespoon coarsely chopped fresh chives

2 slices light rye bread (90g)

1 Heat oil in medium saucepan, add onion, chilli and garlic; cook, stirring, over medium heat, until onion is soft. Stir in paste, then undrained tomatoes and sauces; bring to the boil. Reduce heat; simmer, uncovered, about 5 minutes or until mixture is thickened slightly.
2 Add beans to tomato mixture; cook, stirring, until beans are heated through. Stir in parsley.
3 Meanwhile, toast bread. Serve chilli beans on toast; sprinkle with chives.

notes Chilli beans can be served either hot or cold. Store beans, covered, in the refrigerator for up to three days.
Keep any leftover bread in the freezer to use at a later date.

nutritional count per serving
▶ 6.4g total fat
▶ 1.2g saturated fat
▶ 1411kJ (337 cal)
▶ 42.4g carbohydrate
▶ 15.8g protein
▶ 22.6g fibre

lemon pepper chicken and zucchini salad

PREP + COOK TIME 45 MINUTES SERVES 2

2 teaspoons finely grated lemon rind

1 teaspoon cracked black pepper

¼ cup (60ml) lemon juice

2 chicken breast fillets (300g)

cooking-oil spray

3 medium zucchini (360g)

1 clove garlic, chopped finely

2 green onions (scallions), sliced thinly lengthways

1 medium radicchio (200g) leaves separated

½ cup fresh flat-leaf parsley leaves

1 Combine rind, pepper and 1 tablespoon of the juice in large bowl, add chicken; toss to coat.

2 Lightly spray heated grill plate (or grill or barbecue); cook chicken until cooked through.

3 Thinly slice zucchini lengthways. Cook on grill plate until tender.

4 Whisk remaining juice and the garlic in large bowl, add zucchini and onion; toss gently to combine.

5 Place radicchio on serving plate; top with salad and chicken, sprinkle with parsley.

notes Zucchini colours range from almost black, dark green, pale green, pale green with a grey hue, and yellow. While they are available year round, their peak season is winter through spring. For an extra flavour hit, you could add some chopped fresh tarragon to the salad.

nutritional count per serving

▶ 9.1g total fat

▶ 2.6g saturated fat

▶ 1109kJ (265 cal)

▶ 5.3g carbohydrate

▶ 36.2g protein

▶ 5.9g fibre

DAY 10

tropical fruit lassi

PREP TIME 15 MINUTES **SERVES** 2 (MAKES 2½ CUPS)

½ cup (140g) low-fat plain yogurt or buttermilk

¼ cup (60ml) water

50g (1½ ounces) seeded, peeled, coarsely chopped rockmelon

50g (1½ ounces) peeled, coarsely chopped pineapple

1 small mango (300g), peeled, chopped coarsely

50g (1½ ounces) strawberries, halved

2 teaspoons caster (superfine) sugar

3 ice cubes

1   Blend or process ingredients until smooth.

notes Vary the fruit according to the season and your preference. You need only 50g of both peeled and chopped pineapple and rockmelon for this recipe, so buy the smallest ones you can find. You can eat what's left as part of a fruit salad for your snacks.

DIARY ENTRY

The hunger between meals is certainly not as great anymore. I'm getting used to it. But I won't deny that I could really go for a hamburger right about now.
– Hieu

Took my small elderly dog for a walk, but only a short walk, as she's a bit rickety in the hind legs these days. When she stops dead in her tracks, I just carry her – I figure carrying another 5 kilos is probably good for me.
– Pamela

tomato and kumara rice salad

PREP + COOK TIME 40 MINUTES SERVES 2

½ cup (100g) brown rice

½ small kumara (orange sweet potato) (125g), chopped coarsely

125g (4 ounces) red grape tomatoes, halved

1 green onion (scallion), sliced thinly

¼ cup coarsely chopped fresh basil leaves

20g (¾ ounce) baby rocket leaves (arugula)

BALSAMIC DRESSING

1 tablespoon orange juice

2 teaspoons white balsamic vinegar

1 clove garlic, crushed

1 Cook rice in large saucepan of boiling water, uncovered, about 30 minutes or until tender; drain. Rinse under cold water; drain.
2 Boil, steam or microwave kumara until tender; drain.
3 Make balsamic dressing.
4 Combine rice, kumara and dressing in large bowl with tomato, onion, basil and rocket.

BALSAMIC DRESSING Combine ingredients in screw-top jar; shake well.

note You can substitute white wine vinegar or balsamic vinegar for the white balsamic vinegar, if you like.

nutritional count per serving
▶ 1.5g total fat
▶ 0.3g saturated fat
▶ 1021kJ (244 cal)
▶ 48.9g carbohydrate
▶ 5.8g protein
▶ 4.5g fibre

beef fillet with gremolata and semi-dried tomato polenta

PREP + COOK TIME 30 MINUTES (+ REFRIGERATION) SERVES 2

cooking-oil spray

¾ cup (180ml) water

¾ cup (180ml) vegetable stock

⅓ cup (55g) polenta

2 tablespoons semi-dried tomatoes in oil, drained well, chopped coarsely (see notes)

1 tablespoon finely grated parmesan cheese

250g (8 ounces) piece beef eye fillet

100g (3 ounces) mixed salad leaves

GREMOLATA

¼ cup coarsely chopped fresh flat-leaf parsley

1 clove garlic, crushed

2 teaspoons finely grated lemon rind

2 tablespoons lemon juice

1 Preheat oven to 200°C/400°F. Line oven tray with baking paper. Lightly spray deep 19cm (8-inch) square cake pan.

2 Combine the water and stock in a large saucepan; bring to the boil. Gradually add polenta to liquid, stirring constantly. Reduce heat; cook, stirring constantly, over low heat, about 7 minutes or until polenta thickens. Stir tomato and cheese into polenta; season to taste. Spread mixture into pan to form a 15cm (6-inch) square, using corner as a guide. Cover; refrigerate about 1 hour or until polenta is firm.

3 Meanwhile, make gremolata.

4 Lightly spray heated grill plate (or grill or barbecue); cook beef until browned all over. Place on oven tray; cook, in oven, about 15 minutes (for medium) or until cooked as you like. Cover; stand 10 minutes, then slice thickly.

5 Meanwhile, turn polenta onto board; cut into four squares, cut each square diagonally into two triangles. Cook polenta triangles, in batches, in same heated pan, over medium heat, until browned lightly both sides.

6 To serve, top polenta with beef then gremolata; accompany with salad.

GREMOLATA Combine ingredients in small bowl.

notes Drain the tomatoes on absorbent paper, pressing firmly to remove as much oil as possible. If you have a square 15cm (6-inch) cake pan or container, you can use that rather than the 19cm pan, however, we find that most people have the larger-sized pan rather than the smaller one. You could spread the polenta into a lightly oiled take-away container.

DAY 11

porridge with apple compote

PREP + COOK TIME 20 MINUTES SERVES 2

1 medium apple (150g)

¼ teaspoon ground cinnamon

2 tablespoons water

4 dried apricots, halved

2 teaspoons sultanas

½ cup (45g) rolled oats

½ cup (125ml) skim milk

¾ cup (180ml) boiling water

2 teaspoons brown sugar

1 Peel, core and slice apple thickly. Place apple, cinnamon and the water in medium saucepan; bring to the boil. Reduce heat, simmer, uncovered, 2 minutes.

2 Add apricots and sultanas to pan; simmer, covered, about 5 minutes or until apple is tender.

3 Meanwhile, combine oats, milk and the boiling water in another medium saucepan; bring to the boil. Reduce heat, simmer, uncovered, stirring occasionally, about 5 minutes or until mixture thickens.

4 Serve porridge with compote; sprinkle with brown sugar.

note Any dried fruit, such as prunes, peaches or pears, could be used instead of the apricots.

DIARY ENTRY

I can't believe we are halfway through; the food is delicious and I feel so good. I'm less tired, my skin has cleared up and friends and family have started to notice my weight loss. Today I ate out for lunch with my mum; choosing alternatives to calorie-packed meals is quite simple – go for meals with fresh ingredients and ask for dressings or sauces on the side.
– Emma

Today I felt real cravings for fatty food; I found myself staring longingly at slices of cake and big bowls of pasta. Thank goodness for the tasty scallops at dinner, they felt like a real treat.
– Charlotte

nutritional count per serving
▶ 4.3g total fat
▶ 0.7g saturated fat
▶ 1675kJ (400 cal)
▶ 78.3g carbohydrate
▶ 8.7g protein
▶ 10.8g fibre

turkey vietnamese roll

PREP + COOK TIME 10 MINUTES SERVES 2

1 small carrot (140g)

1 lebanese cucumber (130g)

2 green onions (scallions)

2 white bread rolls (170g)

2 teaspoons reduced-fat mayonnaise

50g (1½ ounces) shaved smoked turkey breast

¼ cup fresh coriander leaves

1 small fresh red thai chilli (serrano), sliced thinly

2 teaspoons light soy sauce

1 Using a vegetable peeler, cut long strips from carrot and cucumber. Thinly slice onions.
2 Split bread rolls lengthways through top, without cutting all the way through.
3 Spread base of each roll with 1 teaspoon mayonnaise; top equally with carrot, cucumber, onion, turkey, coriander and chilli; drizzle with the sauce.

---

nutritional count per serving

▶ 6g total fat   ▶ 48g carbohydrate
▶ 1.3g saturated fat   ▶ 13.5g protein
▶ 1330kJ (318 cal)   ▶ 8g fibre

stir-fried scallops with cherry tomato salsa

PREP + COOK TIME 30 MINUTES SERVES 2

300g (9 ounces) scallops without roe

1 clove garlic, crushed

1 teaspoon olive oil

CHERRY TOMATO SALSA

250g (8 ounces) cherry tomatoes, quartered

1 lebanese cucumber (130g), seeded, chopped finely

1 small red onion (100g), chopped finely

2 green onions (scallions), sliced thinly

1 tablespoon lemon juice

1 small fresh red thai chilli (serrano), sliced thinly

1 Combine scallops with garlic in medium bowl; season. Cover; refrigerate while making salsa.
2 Make cherry tomato salsa.
3 Heat oil in wok; stir-fry scallops, in batches, over high heat, until scallops are browned lightly and cooked as desired. Add scallops to cherry tomato salsa; toss gently.

CHERRY TOMATO SALSA Combine ingredients in large bowl.

nutritional count per serving
▶ 3.6g total fat   ▶ 8.1g carbohydrate
▶ 0.7g saturated fat   ▶ 19.3g protein
▶ 637kJ (152 cal)   ▶ 3.7g fibre

DAY 12

---

bruschetta with strawberry, banana and ricotta

PREP + COOK TIME 25 MINUTES **SERVES** 2

100g (3 ounces) low-fat ricotta cheese

1 tablespoon honey

½ teaspoon finely grated orange rind

¼ teaspoon ground cinnamon

125g (4 ounces) strawberries, sliced thickly

1 small banana (130g), sliced thinly

2 teaspoons light brown sugar

4 slices ciabatta bread (180g)

1 Mix ricotta, honey, rind and cinnamon in small bowl until smooth.
2 Combine strawberries, banana and sugar in small non-stick frying pan; stir gently over low heat until sugar dissolves.
3 Toast bread. Spread with ricotta mixture; top with fruit mixture.

note Use the ciabatta bread left over from the recipe on day 2.

DIARY ENTRY

My task for the day at work was to make 100 quantities of butter cream for a photoshoot. So much butter and sugar! Pamela commented on the irony of someone on a diet smelling so overpoweringly of butter! After a busy day of beating and sifting, the masoor dhal felt like I was having a typical Friday night takeaway, except tastier and healthier!
– Charlotte

It's Friday and I can't say I'm not glad this week is over. Everything was 'hard' this week, and I'd normally resort to food for comfort – now there's an admission I'm not proud of – but I have stayed true to the diet and feel good about that. I know I've lost over 2 kilos and I'm hoping to lose more over the last week or so.
– Pamela

nutritional count per serving
▶ 6.4g total fat
▶ 3.1g saturated fat
▶ 1733kJ (414 cal)
▶ 69.7g carbohydrate
▶ 17.2g protein
▶ 5.1g fibre

tuna and asparagus frittata

PREP + COOK TIME 35 MINUTES SERVES 2

1 large potato (300g), sliced thinly

cooking-oil spray

1 small brown onion (80g), sliced thinly

1 clove garlic, crushed

170g (5½ ounces) asparagus, trimmed, chopped coarsely

185g (6 ounces) canned tuna in spring water, drained

3 eggs, beaten lightly

3 egg whites, beaten lightly

2 tablespoons finely chopped fresh flat-leaf parsley

100g (3 ounces) baby rocket leaves (arugula)

1 medium lemon (140g)

1 Preheat oven to 200°C/400°F.

2 Boil, steam or microwave potato until tender.

3 Lightly spray 20cm (8-inch) (base measurement) ovenproof frying pan; cook onion and garlic, stirring, over medium heat, until onion softens.

4 Combine potato and onion mixture in large bowl with asparagus, tuna, egg, egg white and parsley.

5 Reheat same pan; spray lightly with cooking oil. Spoon frittata mixture into pan; cook, uncovered, over low heat, until egg is beginning to set around the edges. Transfer pan to oven; cook frittata until top is browned lightly and egg is set, about 20 minutes.

6 Serve frittata with rocket and a squeeze of lemon. Season to taste.

notes You can substitute well-drained canned asparagus for the fresh, if desired. Frittata can be made a day ahead; cover, refrigerate. Reheat in microwave oven on MEDIUM (50%) about 2 minutes or until heated through.

nutritional count per serving

▶ 11.8g total fat
▶ 3.4g saturated fat
▶ 1591kJ (380 cal)

▶ 24.3g carbohydrate
▶ 41g protein
▶ 5g fibre

masoor dhal with vegetables

PREP + COOK TIME 30 MINUTES SERVES 2

cooking-oil spray

2 baby eggplants (120g), halved lengthways

2 tablespoons water

1 small brown onion (80g), sliced thinly

1 tablespoon curry paste

1½ cups (375ml) water, extra

1 medium carrot (120g), sliced thickly

1 cup (100g) cauliflower florets

½ cup (100g) dried red lentils

1 medium zucchini (120g), sliced thickly diagonally

50g (1½ ounces) snow peas, trimmed

2 pappadums (30g)

¼ cup fresh coriander (cilantro) leaves

1 Lightly spray heated large saucepan with cooking oil. Cook eggplant, cut-side down, for 3 minutes or until browned. Turn eggplant over; add 1 tablespoon of the water; cook a further 2 minutes or until soft. Remove from pan.

2 Cook onion with the remaining tablespoon of the water in same pan, stirring, over medium heat, until onion softens. Add curry paste; cook, stirring, until mixture is fragrant.

3 Add the extra water, carrot, cauliflower and lentils; bring to the boil. Reduce heat; simmer, covered, about 5 minutes.

4 Add zucchini to pan; cook, uncovered, a further 5 minutes. Add snow peas to pan. Cook, stirring, until lentils are tender. Season to taste.

5 Cook pappadums according to directions on packet. Sprinkle dhal with coriander to serve; accompany with pappadums.

notes Substitute any of your favourite vegetables if you prefer them to the ones suggested in this recipe. A hot curry paste will boost the flavour, however you can use any curry paste you like.

nutritional count per serving

▶ 2.1g total fat

▶ 0.5g saturated fat

▶ 1029kJ (246 cal)

▶ 28.3g carbohydrate

▶ 17.1g protein

▶ 12.2g fibre

DAY 13

---

muffins with poached eggs, ham and herb dressing

PREP + COOK TIME 15 MINUTES **SERVES** 2

1 tablespoon white wine vinegar

2 eggs

1 wholemeal english muffin, halved

60g (2 ounces) baby spinach leaves

100g (3 ounces) light ham

1 tablespoon reduced-fat mayonnaise

2 teaspoons lemon juice

1 tablespoon finely chopped fresh chives

1 Half fill a large deep saucepan with water; bring to the boil. Break one egg into a cup then slide into pan; when both eggs are in the pan, return to the boil. Cover pan, remove from heat; stand 3 minutes or until a light film of egg white sets over yolks.

2 Remove eggs, one at a time, using slotted spoon; briefly place spoon on absorbent paper to blot up any poaching liquid.

3 Toast muffin halves; top each muffin half with spinach, ham and egg. Drizzle with combined mayonnaise, juice and chives.

notes You can use plain white vinegar, if that's what's in your pantry cupboard. You can use a wooden spoon to make a whirlpool in the water before adding the egg, if you like; however, it's best to poach just one egg at a time this way, as it gets a bit tricky whirlpooling the water once there's more than one egg in it.

DIARY ENTRY

I made breakfast and wondered why it was so generous compared to what we've been having. Then, after demolishing the entire thing, I realised that I had eaten the entire recipe of 2 serves.
– Hieu

I've just realised we're over half way through this diet. It has been quite easy, despite the cold weather and the predominantly summery food we've eaten. I've only felt hungry a few times, and when I do, I tell myself 'no pain, no gain' - or loss, in this case.
– Pamela

char-grilled polenta strips with corn salsa

PREP + COOK TIME 30 MINUTES (+ REFRIGERATION) **SERVES** 2

cooking-oil spray

2 cups (500ml) water

½ cup (85g) polenta

1 tablespoon wholegrain mustard

CORN SALSA

1 trimmed corn cob (250g)

1 small red capsicum (bell pepper) (150g), chopped finely

1 small red onion (100g), chopped finely

1 lebanese cucumber (130g), seeded, chopped finely

2 tablespoons coarsely chopped fresh flat-leaf parsley

1 teaspoon finely grated lime rind

2 tablespoons lime juice

1 teaspoon olive oil

1 clove garlic, crushed

2 teaspoons sweet chilli sauce

1 Lightly spray 19cm (8-inch) square cake pan with cooking-oil.

2 Bring the water and a pinch of salt to the boil in a small saucepan. Stir in polenta; cook, stirring, about 7 minutes or until polenta thickens. Season. Stir in mustard until combined; spread polenta into pan to form a 15cm (6-inch) square, using corner as a guide. Cover polenta; refrigerate about 30 minutes or until firm.

3 Meanwhile, make corn salsa.

4 Turn polenta onto board; cut into six rectangles. Lightly spray heated grill plate (or grill or barbecue) with cooking-oil. Cook polenta until browned both sides. Serve polenta cakes with corn salsa.

CORN SALSA Boil, steam or microwave corn until just tender. Drain; cool. Using sharp knife, remove kernels from cob. Combine corn in medium bowl with remaining ingredients.

notes Substitute the fresh corn with a 420g (13½-ounce) can of drained corn kernels, if you prefer. Polenta can be prepared a day ahead. If you have a square 15cm (6-inch) cake pan or container, you can use that rather than the 19cm pan, however, we find that most people have the larger-sized pan rather than the smaller one. You could spread the polenta into a lightly oiled take-away container.

nutritional count per serving
▶ 6.2g total fat
▶ 0.7g saturated fat
▶ 1337kJ (319 cal)
▶ 54.6g carbohydrate
▶ 9.9g protein
▶ 8g fibre

nutritional count per serving
▶ 5.1g total fat
▶ 1.6g saturated fat
▶ 1120kJ (268 cal)
▶ 9.5g carbohydrate
▶ 46.5g protein
▶ 3.9g fibre

warm pork and choy sum salad

PREP + COOK TIME 35 MINUTES SERVES 2

400g (12½ ounces) pork tenderloin

2 tablespoons lime juice

2cm (¾-inch) piece fresh ginger (10g), grated

1 medium carrot (120g)

cooking-oil spray

250g (8 ounces) choy sum, chopped coarsely

1 tablespoon water

¼ cup firmly packed fresh basil leaves

½ cup firmly packed fresh coriander leaves (cilantro)

2 green onions (scallions), sliced thinly

SWEET CHILLI DRESSING

2 teaspoons fish sauce

2 teaspoons sweet chili sauce

2 teaspoons lime juice

1 small fresh red thai chilli (serrano), chopped finely

1 Place pork in large bowl with juice and ginger; toss to coat pork in mixture.

2 Make sweet chilli dressing.

3 Using vegetable peeler, slice carrot into thin ribbons.

4 Lightly spray medium frying pan; cook pork over medium heat about 8 minutes or until browned all over and cooked as desired. Remove from pan; cover to keep warm.

5 Add choy sum to same heated pan with the water; cook, stirring, until choy sum is just wilted.

6 Meanwhile, thickly slice pork. Place choy sum, carrot, herbs and onion in large bowl with dressing; toss gently. Serve pork with salad.

SWEET CHILLI DRESSING Combine ingredients in screw-top jar; shake well.

note Any asian greens can be used in this recipe. Try it with buk choy or gai lan (also known as chinese broccoli). You need one bunch of asian greens for this recipe.

DAY 14

baked ricottas with roasted tomatoes

PREP + COOK TIME 30 MINUTES SERVES 2

cooking-oil spray

2 teaspoons pine nuts

1 clove garlic, crushed

70g (2½ ounces) baby spinach leaves

⅔ cup (160g) low-fat ricotta cheese

1 egg white, beaten lightly

1 tablespoon coarsely chopped fresh chives

250g (8 ounces) baby trussed tomatoes

2 teaspoons balsamic vinegar

1 Preheat oven to 220°C/425°F. Lightly spray two ⅓-cup (80ml) ramekins with cooking oil.
2 Heat large non-stick frying pan over low heat; cook nuts and garlic, stirring, until fragrant. Add spinach, stir until wilted. Cool mixture 10 minutes.
3 Combine ricotta, egg white and chives in medium bowl with spinach mixture; divide the mixture into ramekins.
4 Bake, uncovered, about 20 minutes or until cheese is browned lightly.
5 Meanwhile, toss tomatoes with vinegar; place on oven tray. Roast, uncovered, 10 minutes or until softened. Serve baked ricottas with roasted tomatoes.

note You can make these in a standard muffin pan, if you like; line the holes with paper cases, or a folded square of baking paper, as we did here.

DIARY ENTRY

Today was a complete write off for the diet. Had a huge family gathering, which involved lots of food and wine and laughs. Succeeded in not tucking into my usual 'thirds', which is something. I've decided I'm not going to beat myself up about having a day off, life will always get in the way of a diet at some stage, and there's always tomorrow!
– Charlotte

Loved the pork last night. The trick is to cook pork over a medium to high heat and not for very long, then cover it to keep warm while you make the salad. This way the pork will be tender and juicy – overcooking pork just dries it out and spoils the texture and taste.
– Pamela

nutritional count per serving
▶ 9.8g total fat
▶ 4.6g saturated fat
▶ 686kJ (164 cal)
▶ 5.1g carbohydrate
▶ 12.2g protein
▶ 3.4g fibre

chilli-prawn noodle salad

PREP + COOK TIME 30 MINUTES **SERVES** 2

500g (1 pound) unshelled cooked medium prawns (shrimp)

2 tablespoons lime juice

1 tablespoon sweet chilli sauce

1 fresh long red chilli, sliced thinly

1 fresh long green chilli, sliced thinly

1 teaspoon white (granulated) sugar

100g (3 ounces) bean thread noodles

½ cup fresh mint leaves

50g (1½ ounces) snow pea sprouts

1 Shell and devein prawns, leaving tails intact. Combine prawns in large bowl with juice, sauce, chillies and sugar.
2 Place noodles in large heatproof bowl, cover with boiling water, stand until tender; drain.
3 Add noodles to prawn mixture with mint and sprouts; toss gently to combine.

note We served the salad on butter lettuce leaves, however, this is optional.

nutritional count per serving
- ▶ 1.1g total fat
- ▶ 0.2g saturated fat
- ▶ 1170kJ (280 cal)
- ▶ 44.2g carbohydrate
- ▶ 27.4g protein
- ▶ 4g fibre

moroccan lamb with couscous

PREP + COOK TIME 30 MINUTES (+ REFRIGERATION) **SERVES** 2

4 lamb fillets (350g)

2 teaspoons each ground cumin and coriander

½ teaspoon ground cinnamon

½ cup (140g) low-fat plain yogurt

½ cup (100g) couscous

½ cup (125ml) boiling water

2 tablespoons dried currants

2 teaspoons finely grated lemon rind

2 teaspoons lemon juice

¼ cup fresh coriander leaves (cilantro)

1 Combine lamb, spices and ¼ cup of the yogurt in medium bowl, cover; refrigerate for 3 hours or overnight.

2 Cook lamb on heated oiled grill plate (or grill or barbecue) until cooked as desired. Cover; stand 5 minutes, then slice thinly.

3 Meanwhile, combine couscous and the water in large heatproof bowl, cover; stand 5 minutes or until liquid is absorbed, fluffing with fork occasionally. Stir in currants, rind, juice, fresh coriander and lamb; toss with fork to combine.

4 Serve lamb and couscous with remaining yogurt. Serve with a squeeze of lemon, if you like.

tips Marinate the lamb the night before. You can substitute some finely chopped preserved lemon for the lemon juice and rind in the couscous.

nutritional count per serving

▶ 11.9g total fat

▶ 3.7g saturated fat

▶ 2194kJ (524 cal)

▶ 52.2g carbohydrate

▶ 49.8g protein

▶ 2.1g fibre

DAY 15

strawberry and rhubarb muffins

PREP + COOK TIME 35 MINUTES **MAKES** 24

30g low-fat margarine

1½ cups (240g) wholemeal self-raising flour

¼ cup (55g) firmly packed brown sugar

½ teaspoon ground cinnamon

½ teaspoon vanilla extract

⅓ cup (80ml) skim milk

1 egg, beaten lightly

60g (2 ounces) small strawberries

½ cup (55g) finely chopped rhubarb

1½ tablespoons apple sauce

1 Preheat oven to 180°C/350°F. Grease 24-hole mini muffin pan (1-tablespoon/20ml).
2 Melt margarine; cool slightly. Combine flour, sugar and cinnamon in large bowl. Add vanilla, margarine, milk and egg; mix to combine.
3 Slice strawberries thinly. Reserve 24 slices. Chop remaining slices finely; gently stir into batter with the rhubarb and apple sauce.
4 Spoon mixture into pan holes; top each with a strawberry slice. Bake muffins about 15 minutes.

notes You need about 2 large trimmed rhubarb stems for this recipe. Muffins can be served warm or at room temperature.

DIARY ENTRY

I lost another 1.5kg this week, which is great, but I did notice the difference in my moods and energy levels by not exercising, so I'm back out hitting the pavement.
– Emma

Well, excitement plus, I was allowed three tiny muffins for breakfast! Surprisingly, I found them quite satisfying; the secret is to eat them slowly.
– Pamela

nutritional count per muffin

▶ 1.2g total fat
▶ 9g carbohydrate
▶ 0.2g saturated fat
▶ 1.7g protein
▶ 233kJ (56 cal)
▶ 1.3g fibre

This recipe makes 24 muffins. Have 3 for breakfast, and freeze remaining muffins for another day's breakfast, or to eat as a snack.

roasted pumpkin and tomato soup

PREP + COOK TIME 50 MINUTES **SERVES** 2

600g (1¼ pounds) pumpkin, cut into 2cm (¾-inch) pieces

cooking-oil spray

1 small red onion (100g), chopped finely

1 medium ripe tomato (150g), finely chopped

1 clove garlic, crushed

1½ tablespoons tomato paste

⅓ cup (65g) brown rice

1 cup (250ml) water

3 cups (750ml) chicken or vegetable stock

1 tablespoon coarsely chopped smoked almonds

1 Preheat oven to 200°C/400°F.

2 Place pumpkin in medium baking dish; spray with cooking oil. Roast about 20 minutes or until pumpkin is browned lightly.

3 Meanwhile, heat lightly oiled medium saucepan over medium heat; cook onion, tomato and garlic, stirring, until onion is soft. Stir in paste, rice, the water and stock; bring to the boil, simmer, uncovered, about 30 minutes or until rice is tender.

4 Divide pumpkin among serving bowls; top with soup. Sprinkle with almonds to serve. Serve topped with fresh thyme, if you like.

tips Under-ripe tomatoes should be left at room temperature to ripen and develop colour and flavour. All tomatoes should be taken out of the refrigerator at least half an hour before use. Smoked almonds are available from most major supermarkets.

nutritional count per serving
- 8g total fat
- 2.3g saturated fat
- 1512kJ (361 cal)
- 52.7g carbohydrate
- 15.9g protein
- 7.4g fibre

stir-fried thai chicken

PREP + COOK TIME 35 MINUTES SERVES 2

100g (3 ounces) dried rice stick noodles

½ teaspoon olive oil

150g (4½ ounces) chicken breast fillet, sliced thinly

100g (3 ounces) green beans, halved

1 clove garlic, crushed

1cm (½-inch) piece fresh ginger (5g), grated

1 tablespoon sweet chilli sauce

1 tablespoon water

250g (8 ounces) baby buk choy, halved lengthways

1 tablespoon fish sauce

1½ tablespoons lime juice

3 green onions (scallions), sliced thinly

1 cup bean sprouts (80g)

½ cup firmly packed fresh coriander leaves (cilantro)

½ cup firmly packed fresh mint leaves

1 small fresh red thai chilli (serrano), sliced thinly

1 Place noodles in large heatproof bowl, cover with boiling water; stand until just tender, drain.

2 Meanwhile, heat oil in wok over medium heat; stir-fry chicken until just cooked. Add beans, garlic, ginger, sweet chilli sauce and the water to wok; stir-fry until beans are almost tender.

3 Add buk choy, fish sauce, juice, onion, sprouts and half the herbs to wok; stir-fry until hot.

4 Serve chicken mixture on noodles; sprinkle with chilli and remaining herbs. Accompany with lime wedges, if you like.

note Cook chicken for day 16 lunch while preparing tonight's dinner.

nutritional count per serving
▶ 6.5g total fat
▶ 1.5g saturated fat
▶ 1309kJ (313 cal)
▶ 38.9g carbohydrate
▶ 27g protein
▶ 8g fibre

DAY 16

fruit salad with honey yogurt

PREP TIME 15 MINUTES **SERVES** 2

½ cup (140g) low-fat plain yogurt

1 tablespoon honey

100g (3 ounces) peeled, coarsely chopped pineapple

100g (3 ounces) seeded, peeled, coarsely chopped rockmelon

125g (4 ounces) strawberries, halved

125g (4 ounces) blueberries

1 medium banana (200g), sliced thinly

1 tablespoon passionfruit pulp

1 teaspoon lime juice

6 fresh mint leaves

1 Combine yogurt and honey in small bowl.
2 Just before serving, combine remaining ingredients in large bowl; serve with honey yogurt.

notes You only need small quantities of the pineapple and rockmelon for this recipe, so buy the smallest ones you can find. Two passionfruit will supply the right amount of pulp.
Lime juice not only adds flavour to this recipe, but also prevents the banana from discolouring. Honey yogurt can be made a day ahead; store, covered, in the refrigerator.

DIARY ENTRY

Well, so much for my early exercise... I kept hitting the snooze button, and chose sleep over walking; there is always tomorrow, so no guilt today.
– Emma

I loved today's dinner. I'm really starting to get used to the smaller portions and I'm hungry less often. Having snacks throughout the day really helps.
– Hieu

nutritional count per serving
▶ 0.5g total fat
▶ 0g saturated fat
▶ 1019kJ (243 cal)
▶ 47.3g carbohydrate
▶ 8.1g protein
▶ 7.6g fibre

chicken and tikka pitta

PREP + COOK TIME 35 MINUTES SERVES 2

1 chicken breast fillet (150g)

2 teaspoons tikka masala curry paste

¼ cup (70g) low-fat plain yogurt

cooking-oil spray

½ lebanese cucumber (65g), seeded, chopped finely

2 tablespoons coarsely chopped fresh mint

½ small red onion (50g), chopped finely

2 wholemeal pocket pitta breads (70g)

50g (1½ ounces) mixed salad leaves

1 Cut chicken fillet in half horizontally. Combine chicken in large bowl with curry paste and 1 tablespoon of the yogurt.

2 Lightly spray heated grill plate (or grill or barbecue); cook chicken until browned all over and cooked through. Cover; stand 5 minutes, then slice thinly.

3 Meanwhile, combine cucumber, mint, onion and remaining yogurt in medium bowl.

4 Just before serving, top pitta breads with salad leaves then chicken and yogurt mixture. Roll to enclose filling.

tip Cook the chicken the night before.

---

nutritional count per serving

▶ 6.8g total fat
▶ 22.2g carbohydrate
▶ 1.7g saturated fat
▶ 22.5g protein
▶ 1026kJ (245 cal)
▶ 3.7g fibre

blue-eye fillets with vegetables

PREP + COOK TIME 30 MINUTES SERVES 2

2 teaspoons olive oil

1 medium carrot (120g), cut into matchsticks

1 small red capsicum (150g), sliced thinly

2cm (¾-inch) piece fresh ginger (10g), grated

1 clove garlic, crushed

125g (4 ounces) choy sum, chopped coarsely

4 green onions (scallions), sliced thinly

1 tablespoon light soy sauce

2 x 200g (6½-ounce) blue-eye fillets

1 Heat half the oil in large frying pan; cook carrot, capsicum, ginger and garlic, stirring, over high heat, about 2 minutes or until softened.

2 Add choy sum, half the onion and the sauce; cook, stirring, about 1 minute or until choy sum is wilted. Remove from pan; cover to keep warm.

3 Heat remaining oil in same pan; cook fish, over medium heat, about 3 minutes each side or until browned lightly and cooked as desired.

4 Divide vegetables between serving plates; top with fish, sprinkle with remaining onion. Accompany with lemon wedges, if you like.

tip Tuna and swordfish are both excellent substitutes for blue-eye.

nutritional count per serving

▶ 9.4g total fat   ▶ 6.8g carbohydrate
▶ 2.1g saturated fat   ▶ 45.5g protein
▶ 1284kJ (307 cal)   ▶ 6.1g fibre

DAY 17

breakfast fry-up

PREP + COOK TIME 30 MINUTES **SERVES** 2

2 medium egg (plum) tomatoes (150g), quartered

1 tablespoon balsamic vinegar

cooking-oil spray

150g (4½ ounces) button mushrooms, halved

100g (3 ounces) shaved light ham

2 slices wholemeal bread (90g)

¼ cup loosely packed fresh basil leaves

2 tablespoons loosely packed fresh coriander leaves (cilantro)

1 Preheat oven to 200°C/400°F.

2 Combine tomato and half the vinegar in medium shallow baking dish; spray with oil. Roast, uncovered, about 20 minutes.

3 Lightly spray medium non-stick frying pan; cook mushrooms and remaining vinegar, stirring, over medium heat, until tender. Transfer mixture to serving dishes; cover to keep warm.

4 Heat ham in same pan.

5 Meanwhile, toast bread. Stir herbs into mushroom mixture. Serve ham, mushroom and tomato mixtures with toast.

DIARY ENTRY

I've noticed my energy levels are so much higher than before I started the diet. I find it easier to wake up in the morning and I take two stairs at a time leaving the train station. This truly is the best diet I have ever done, and trust me, I have done a lot of them.
– Charlotte

I dragged myself and the dog out of bed at 5.30am and hit the pavement — the dog was a little more excited than I. I find exercise a chore, but I have to say, as painful as it is, I feel more alive after the walk, and focus better throughout the day.
– Emma

nutritional count per serving
▶ 6.2g total fat
▶ 1.5g saturated fat
▶ 909kJ (217 cal)
▶ 19.7g carbohydrate
▶ 17g protein
▶ 5.9g fibre

beetroot and orange salad

PREP + COOK TIME 15 MINUTES SERVES 2

340g (11 ounces) asparagus spears, trimmed

100g (3 ounces) curly endive, leaves separated

125g (4 ounces) red witlof, leaves separated

425g (13½ ounces) canned baby beetroot, drained, halved

2 teaspoons toasted pine nuts

2 medium blood oranges (480g), segmented

75g (2½ ounces) low-fat fetta cheese

ORANGE DRESSING

2 tablespoons strained blood orange juice

2 teaspoons lemon juice

2 teaspoons olive oil

1 tablespoon white wine vinegar

1 Make orange dressing.

2 Cook asparagus in medium saucepan of boiling water, 1 minute; drain, rinse under cold water, drain.

3 Arrange leaves on serving plates; top with beetroot, nuts, asparagus, orange segments and fetta. Drizzle with orange dressing.

ORANGE DRESSING Combine ingredients in screw-top jar; shake well.

note Blood oranges are available in winter. At other times use navel oranges instead. Segment the oranges over a bowl to catch any juice; use this in the dressing.

nutritional count per serving

▶ 13.2g total fat   ▶ 31.1g carbohydrate
▶ 4.3g saturated fat   ▶ 18.7g protein
▶ 1427kJ (341 cal   ▶ 11.6g fibre

pork and thyme risotto

PREP + COOK TIME 45 MINUTES SERVES 2

250g (8 ounces) pork fillets

2 teaspoons teriyaki marinade

1 teaspoon finely grated orange rind

cooking-oil spray

1 clove garlic, crushed

1 small brown onion (80g), chopped finely

⅔ cup (130g) arborio rice

1½ cups (375ml) chicken stock

75g (2½ ounces) baby spinach leaves

1 tablespoon coarsely chopped fresh lemon thyme

1 Combine pork with marinade and rind in small bowl; toss to coat.

2 Lightly spray large saucepan; cook garlic and onion, stirring, over medium heat, until onion softens. Add rice and stock, bring to the boil. Reduce heat; simmer, covered, 15 minutes, stirring halfway through cooking. Remove from heat; cover, stand 10 minutes.

3 Meanwhile, lightly spray heated non-stick frying pan; cook pork, over medium heat, for about 8 minutes, turning occasionally, or until browned all over and cooked as desired. Cover; stand 5 minutes, then slice thinly.

4 Gently stir spinach, thyme and pork into rice mixture.

nutritional count per serving

▶ 4.2g total fat   ▶ 55.4g carbohydrate
▶ 1.5g saturated fat   ▶ 35.6g protein
▶ 1716kJ (410 cal)   ▶ 2.4g fibre

DAY 18

morning trifles

PREP TIME 20 MINUTES **SERVES** 2

2 tablespoons barley flakes

2 tablespoons rice flakes

2 tablespoons triticale flakes

125g (4 ounces) strawberries, hulled

½ cup (140g) low-fat vanilla yogurt

2 tablespoons passionfruit pulp

1 Combine cereals in small bowl.

2 Cut three strawberries in half; Slice remaining strawberries thinly.

3 Divide cereal mixture between serving bowls; layer over the strawberry slices, passionfruit pulp and yogurt. Top with strawberry halves to serve.

notes You need about three passionfruit for this recipe. You could layer these trifles in two 1-cup (250ml) glasses, for a prettier look.

DIARY ENTRY

Had a busy day in the test kitchen second testing recipes and re-checking recipes from reader's queries. It was nice to sit down in the middle of the day and have the salmon pasta salad (pasta being my all-time love). I noticed I couldn't finish my serving, something traditionally completely unheard of from me, fingers crossed this means my stomach is shrinking.
– Charlotte

Last night's dinner was a really yummy risotto-like dish, the only difference being, it was a risotto that didn't need constant stirring – it worked by the absorption method of cooking rice, the result wasn't as creamy as the 'proper' way, but was still mighty fine and tasty.
– Pamela

nutritional count per serving
▶ 0.9g total fat
▶ 0.1g saturated fat
▶ 650kJ (155 cal)
▶ 26.3g carbohydrate
▶ 8.5g protein
▶ 6g fibre

salmon pasta salad

PREP + COOK TIME 20 MINUTES SERVES 2

150g wholewheat penne pasta

¼ cup (70g) low-fat plain yogurt

1 teaspoon wholegrain mustard

1½ tablespoons oil-free italian dressing

1 tablespoon water

210g (6½ ounces) canned red salmon, drained, skin and bones removed

2 teaspoons rinsed, drained baby capers

1 stalk celery (150g), trimmed, sliced thinly

1 lebanese cucumber (130g), sliced thinly

1 tablespoon finely chopped fresh dill

2 teaspoons finely grated lemon rind

1 Cook pasta in large saucepan of boiling water until just tender; drain. Rinse under cold water; drain.
2 Meanwhile, whisk yogurt, mustard, dressing and the water in small bowl until smooth.
3 Place pasta in large bowl with flaked salmon, capers, celery, cucumber, dill and rind. Just before serving, drizzle salad with dressing; toss gently to combine. Serve with lemon cheeks, if you like.

nutritional count per serving
▶ 7.4g total fat
▶ 1.9g saturated fat
▶ 1799kJ (429 cal)
▶ 53.7g carbohydrate
▶ 30.8g protein
▶ 9.4g fibre

roasted red capsicum tarts

PREP + COOK TIME 50 MINUTES **SERVES** 4

cooking-oil spray

1 medium red capsicum (bell pepper) (200g)

1 large brown onion (200g), sliced thinly

1½ tablespoons balsamic vinegar

1½ tablespoons light brown sugar

2 sheets fillo pastry

2 tablespoons fresh basil leaves

2 tablespoons shaved parmesan cheese

100g (3 ounces) mixed salad leaves

2 teaspoons oil-free italian dressing

1 Lightly spray two 12cm (4¾-inch) round loose-based quiche pans.

2 Preheat grill (broiler). Quarter capsicum, discard seeds and membranes. Roast under hot grill, skin-side up, until skin blisters and blackens. Cover capsicum pieces in plastic or paper for 5 minutes, then peel away skin. Slice capsicum into thin strips.

3 Preheat oven to 220°C/400°F.

4 Heat large frying pan over medium heat; cook onion and vinegar, stirring, about 3 minutes or until onion softens. Add sugar; cook, stirring, about 5 minutes or until sugar dissolves and mixture thickens. Remove from heat; combine with capsicum.

5 Cut each pastry sheet into eight rectangles. Place one pastry rectangle in one quiche pan, spray with oil; top with another pastry rectangle, placing corners just to the right of previous rectangle corners. Repeat layering, using eight pastry rectangles in each quiche pan. Place pans on oven tray; bake, uncovered, about 3 minutes or until pastry is beginning to crisp.

6 Spoon capsicum mixture into pastry cases; sprinkle with basil and cheese. Bake, uncovered, about 5 minutes or until hot.

7 Just before serving, toss salad leaves with dressing; serve with tarts.

note Line quiche pans one at a time. Keep the remaining pastry sheet covered with a damp clean tea towel, to stop it drying out while lining the first quiche pan.

nutritional count per serving
▶ 4.3g total fat
▶ 1.7g saturated fat
▶ 746kJ (178 cal)
▶ 27.8g carbohydrate
▶ 7.6g protein
▶ 2.6g fibre

DAY 19

banana smoothie

PREP TIME 5 MINUTES **SERVES** 2 (MAKES 500ML)

1 cup (250ml) skim milk

1 medium banana (200g), chopped coarsely

¼ cup (70g) low-fat plain yogurt

2 teaspoons honey

2 teaspoons unprocessed bran

¼ teaspoon ground cinnamon

1 Blend or process ingredients until smooth.

tip Use frozen bananas or add ice cubes to the blender for a thicker smoothie.

DIARY ENTRY

The family is having a bit of a knees-up tonight to celebrate a birthday, so I will probably break the diet... in a very minor way, of course! Restraint is my new middle name...I took my own veal cutlet and salad, and passed on the lemon meringue pie, which I had made. Not a drop of Champagne passed my lips.
- Pamela

I'll make a confession... I didn't eat the diet dinner tonight as I had a dinner date! Thinking that bringing my own box of food would be a turn off, I decided on lean meat and vegetables...and a glass of wine. Thanks to the diet, though, I felt trim and terrific!
- Charlotte

nutritional count per 1 cup (250ml)
▶ 0.3g total fat   ▶ 26.7g carbohydrate
▶ 0.1g saturated fat   ▶ 6.7g protein
▶ 591kJ (141 cal)   ▶ 2.2g fibre

gourmet chicken sandwiches

PREP + COOK TIME 30 MINUTES **SERVES** 2

2 tablespoons drained semi-dried tomatoes in oil

2 teaspoons coarsely chopped fresh rosemary

1 tablespoon water

105g (3½ ounces) long loaf turkish bread

30g (1 ounce) baby rocket leaves (arugula)

½ lebanese cucumber (65g), sliced thinly

200g (6½ ounces) barbecued chicken, shredded coarsely

½ small red onion (50g), sliced thinly

2 tablespoons low-fat yogurt

1 Drain tomatoes on absorbent paper; pressing firmly to remove as much oil as possible. Quarter tomatoes. Using mortar and pestle, crush tomatoes with rosemary and the water until combined.

2 Halve bread, slice pieces horizontally; toast both sides. Top with rocket, tomato mixture, cucumber, chicken and onion. Drizzle over yogurt to serve.

notes Instead of barbecued chicken, you can poach 200g (6½ ounces) chicken the night before; store, covered, in the refrigerator. We used a quarter of a long loaf of turkish bread. Wrap the remaining onion half to use on day 20, 'mediterranean lamb burgers', page 104.

nutritional count per serving
▶ 9.8g total fat
▶ 2.5g saturated fat
▶ 1537kJ (367 cal)
▶ 32.5g carbohydrate
▶ 34.2g protein
▶ 3.9g fibre

marjoram and lemon-grilled veal chops with greek salad

PREP + COOK TIME 35 MINUTES SERVES 2

½ teaspoon finely grated lemon rind

1½ tablespoons lemon juice

2 teaspoons finely chopped fresh marjoram

1 teaspoon olive oil

2 x 200g (6½-ounce) veal chops

cooking-oil spray

GREEK SALAD

⅓ cup (50g) seeded black olives

100g (3 ounces) low-fat fetta cheese, chopped coarsely

3 medium egg (plum) tomatoes (225g), chopped coarsely

1 small red capsicum (bell pepper) (150g), chopped coarsely

1 lebanese cucumber (130g), chopped coarsely

1 stalk celery (150g), trimmed, sliced thinly

2 teaspoons fresh marjoram leaves

LEMON DRESSING

1 clove garlic, crushed

2 tablespoons lemon juice

1 teaspoon olive oil

1 Combine rind, juice, marjoram and oil in large bowl; add veal, toss to coat.
2 Meanwhile, make greek salad. Make lemon dressing.
3 Lightly spray heated grill plate (or grill or barbecue); cook veal about 3 minutes each side or until cooked as desired.
4 Pour dressing over salad; toss gently to combine. Serve veal with salad.

GREEK SALAD Combine ingredients in large bowl.

LEMON DRESSING Combine ingredients in screw-top jar; shake well.

nutritional count per serving
▶ 18.9g total fat
▶ 7.1g saturated fat
▶ 1073kJ (400 cal)
▶ 8.3g carbohydrate
▶ 45.4g protein
▶ 5.1g fibre

DAY 20

eggs with asparagus, grilled ham and onion jam

PREP + COOK TIME 25 MINUTES **SERVES** 2

cooking-oil spray

1 medium red onion (170g), sliced thinly

1 tablespoon balsamic vinegar

2 tablespoons light brown sugar

1 tablespoon water

50g (1½ ounces) shaved light leg ham

340g (11 ounces) asparagus, trimmed

2 eggs

1 To make onion jam: Lightly spray medium non-stick frying pan; cook onion, stirring, over medium heat until almost soft. Stir in vinegar and sugar; cook, stirring, until sugar dissolves. Stir in water; simmer, uncovered, about 10 minutes or until onion caramelises, cool.

2 Preheat grill (broiler). Place ham, in single layer, on oven tray; cook under hot grill until browned lightly.

3 Boil, steam or microwave asparagus until just tender; drain.

4 Heat same pan over medium-high heat; fry eggs until cooked as desired. Serve eggs with asparagus, ham and onion jam.

note Onion jam can be made a day ahead; keep, covered, in the refrigerator. To serve warm, place in microwave-safe bowl, reheat in microwave on MEDIUM (50%) until warm.

DIARY ENTRY

Cocktails with my girlfriends tonight! A girl's gotta do what a girl's gotta do, however I don't want to go off the diet so close to the end, so I had vodka and mineral water throughout the night. So many of my girlfriends commented on how much weight I have lost. I can't wait until I weigh in tomorrow to see how much I have lost.
– Charlotte

Today and tomorrow to go and I've lost just a tad under 3 kilos, which is good considering the tastings and lack of exercise – let's face it, the more you have to lose, the quicker those first few kilos will disappear. The next batch of three or four kilos are harder to lose, but, I'm a woman on a mission. This diet has given me the impetus to carry on eating in a sensible way until I reach a reasonable weight.
– Pamela

mediterranean lamb burgers

PREP + COOK TIME 25 MINUTES SERVES 2

3 lamb fillets (200g), chopped coarsely

1 egg white

½ cup (35g) stale wholemeal breadcrumbs

2 teaspoons fresh rosemary sprigs

2 teaspoons packed fresh mint leaves

1 teaspoon finely grated lemon rind

½ clove garlic, halved

2 teaspoons tomato paste

cooking-oil spray

50g (1½ ounces) mixed salad leaves

1 small tomato (90g), sliced thinly

½ small red onion (50g), sliced thinly

2 wholemeal bread rolls (140g) split in half

YOGURT SAUCE

⅓ cup (95g) low-fat plain yogurt

½ clove garlic, crushed

1 tablespoon finely chopped fresh mint leaves

½ lebanese cucumber (65g), seeded, chopped finely

1 Process lamb, egg white, breadcrumbs, herbs, rind, garlic and paste until smooth. Using wet hands, shape mixture into two patties.

2 Light spray heated large non-stick pan; cook patties, over medium heat, until browned both sides and cooked through.

3 Make yogurt sauce.

4 Sandwich salad leaves, tomato, patties, onion and yogurt sauce between rolls.

YOGURT SAUCE Combine ingredients in small bowl.

nutritional count per serving
- ▶ 8.6g total fat
- ▶ 2.4g saturated fat
- ▶ 1688kJ (403 cal)
- ▶ 41g carbohydrate
- ▶ 35.7g protein
- ▶ 6.4g fibre

ratatouille pizzas

PREP + COOK TIME 35 MINUTES SERVES 2

1 x 25cm (10-inch) round pizza base (180g)

2 tablespoons tomato paste

80g (2½ ounces) each drained char-grilled eggplant, zucchini and capsicum (bell pepper)

50g (1½ ounces) bocconcini cheese, torn

1 tablespoon fresh basil leaves

100g (3 ounces) rocket leaves (arugula)

2 teaspoons balsamic vinegar

1 Preheat oven to 240°C/475°F. Lightly oil oven tray; place in heated oven for 5 minutes.
2 Place pizza base on tray, spread with paste. Top with eggplant, zucchini, capsicum and cheese; season.
3 Bake pizza about 15 minutes or until base is browned and crisp.
4 Top pizza with basil; serve with combined rocket and vinegar.

tip Make sure you pat dry the char-grilled vegetables with absorbent paper to remove as much excess oil as possible. If you can't buy char-grilled zucchini, you can make your own; use a mandoline or vegetable peeler to thinly slice one large zucchini lengthways, then cook the slices on a heated oiled grill plate until browned lightly and tender.

nutritional count per serving
▶ 14.6g total fat
▶ 3.6g saturated fat
▶ 1639kJ (391 cal)
▶ 53g carbohydrate
▶ 14.3g protein
▶ 5.9g fibre

DAY 21

buttermilk pancakes with golden pears

PREP + COOK TIME 35 MINUTES **SERVES** 2 (MAKES 4)

½ cup (75g) self-raising flour

½ cup (125ml) buttermilk

1 egg white

cooking-oil spray

GOLDEN PEARS

2 corella pears (200g), peeled, halved, seeds removed

1½ tablespoons golden syrup

1 cup (250ml) water

2 teaspoons lemon juice

1 teaspoon cornflour

1 tablespoon water, extra

1 Make golden pears.

2 Sift flour into small bowl; gradually whisk in combined buttermilk and egg white to make a smooth batter.

3 Lightly spray large heated non-stick frying pan. Pour ¼ cup batter into pan; use the back of a spoon to spread the batter into a 10cm (4-inch) round shape. Cook, over low heat, about 2 minutes or until bubbles appear on the surface. Turn pancake; cook until lightly browned on the other side. Remove from pan; cover to keep warm. Repeat with remaining batter to make 3 more pancakes. Serve pancakes with pears and syrup.

GOLDEN PEARS Place pears in small saucepan with golden syrup, the water and juice; bring to the boil. Reduce heat, simmer, uncovered, turning occasionally, about 15 minutes or until pears are just tender. Remove pears from syrup; reserve syrup. Stir blended cornflour and the extra water into reserved syrup; stir over heat until the mixture boils and thickens.

note Cook the recipe just before serving.

DIARY ENTRY

I haven't been this weight since high school; bring on the skinny jeans.
– Charlotte

Had lunch at a restaurant today, so I couldn't have my diet lunch. But I settled for the healthiest option on the menu.
– Hieu

I'm going to continue this healthy low-fat eating and include my family so we can all have a healthier way of life.
– Emma

I wore a pair of jeans that were way too tight just three weeks ago. The loss makes such a difference to the way you feel and look.
– Pamela

nutritional count per serving
▶ 1.9g total fat
▶ 0.9g saturated fat
▶ 1256kJ (300 cal)
▶ 61.2g carbohydrate
▶ 8.6g protein
▶ 3.4g fibre

chicken and green mango salad

PREP + COOK TIME 30 MINUTES SERVES 2

300g (9½ ounces) barbecued chicken, shredded coarsely

1 green mango (350g), cut into matchsticks

½ small red onion (50g), sliced thinly

60g baby mizuna leaves

¼ cup firmly packed fresh coriander leaves (cilantro)

1 medium carrot (120g), cut into matchsticks

¼ cup firmly packed fresh mint leaves

SWEET CHILLI DRESSING

2 tablespoons lime juice

1 tablespoon fish sauce

1 tablespoon sweet chilli sauce

2 teaspoons grated palm sugar

1 Make sweet chilli dressing.
2 Combine ingredients with sweet chilli dressing in medium bowl; toss well. Serve with a squeeze of lime, if you like.

SWEET CHILLI DRESSING Combine ingredients in screw-top jar; shake well.

note Instead of barbecued chicken, you can poach 300g (9½ ounces) chicken the night before; store, covered, in the refrigerator.

nutritional count per serving
- ▶ 3.8g total fat
- ▶ 1g saturated fat
- ▶ 1436kJ (343 cal)
- ▶ 32.1g carbohydrate
- ▶ 49.3g protein
- ▶ 4.4g fibre

roasted ocean trout and asian greens

PREP + COOK TIME 30 MINUTES SERVES 2

2 x 200g (6½-ounce) ocean trout fillets

6 kaffir lime leaves

5cm (2-inch) stick fresh lemon grass (10g), chopped finely

½ teaspoon sesame oil

250g (4 ounces) baby buk choy, halved

6 green onions (scallions), trimmed

1 teaspoon light soy sauce

2 tablespoons sweet chilli sauce

1½ tablespoons lime juice

1 Preheat oven to 180°C/350°F.

2 Place fish fillets on 30cm x 30cm (12-inch x 12-inch) piece of baking paper; top with lime leaves and lemon grass. Gather paper at top and fold sides and top into pleats to form a parcel. Place on baking tray. Bake about 8 minutes or until cooked as you like.

3 Just before serving, heat oil in wok; stir-fry buk choy, onion and soy sauce, over medium heat, until vegetables just wilt.

4 Drizzle combined sweet chilli sauce and juice over fish; serve with vegetables, and a squeeze of lime, if you like.

nutritional count per serving
- 9.2g total fat
- 2g saturated fat
- 1212kJ (290 cal)
- 10.1g carbohydrate
- 40.6g protein
- 1.7g fibre

SNACKS

carrot sticks with salsa
Cut 2 small carrots into sticks. Serve with ⅓ cup store-bought tomato salsa.

strawberries
Wash and hull 250g (8 ounces) strawberries.

grapes
250g (8 ounces) red grapes.

cherries
250g (8 ounces) cherries.

avocado on corn thins
Spread ½ small avocado over 4 corn thins; season to taste.

bananas
2 small bananas

rice cakes with cottage cheese Spread ⅓ cup low-fat cottage cheese over 4 rice thins. Thinly slice 1 small tomato. Serve rice thins topped with tomato; season to taste.

rice crackers with chive cream cheese Serve 20 plain rice crackers with ⅓ cup packaged light chive and onion cream cheese.

popcorn (4 cups)
Place ⅓ cup popping corn in large saucepan, tightly cover with lid. Turn heat to high; wait for the popping to start, then turn off heat and wait for popping to stop before removing lid.

celery with spicy capsicum dip Cut 2 trimmed celery stalks into 4cm (1½-inch) sticks. Serve celery sticks with two tablespoons of store-bought low-fat spicy capsicum dip.

crumpets with honey
Toast 2 crumpets; drizzle 1 tablespoon of honey over crumpets.

strawberry smoothie
Blend or process 2 cups skim milk with 250g (8 ounces) fresh hulled strawberries until smooth.

orange
2 medium oranges

pear
2 small pears

kiwi fruit
4 kiwi fruit

cucumber with cheese
Cut 1 lebanese cucumber
into sticks. Serve with
⅓ cup low-fat cottage
cheese; season to taste.

watermelon
Cut 400g (12½ ounces)
watermelon into wedges.
Watermelon can be peeled
and frozen in an air-tight
container for an icy treat.

mixed berry salad
Combine 80g (2½ ounces)
hulled strawberries, 80g
(2½ ounces) blueberries
and 80g (2½ ounces)
raspberries in a small bowl.

rockmelon
Cut 400g (12½ ounces)
rockmelon into wedges.

fruit pops
Cut 250g (8 ounces) seedless
watermelon into 3cm (1¼-inch)
pieces, halve and thickly slice
1 medium kiwi fruit, segment
1 medium mandarin, halve 125g
(4 ounces) strawberries. Thread
fruit onto four skewers. Cover with
foil; freeze 3 hours or overnight.
Serve skewers with ½ cup low-fat
passionfruit yogurt.

**capsicum sticks with
hummus** Cut 1 small (150g)
red capsicum into strips;
serve with 2 tablespoons
low-fat hummus.

peas with cream cheese
Trim 100g (3 ounces) snow
peas and 100g (3 ounces)
sugar snap peas; serve with
⅓ cup light cream cheese.
Season to taste.

tropical juice
Push ½ small peeled and
chopped pineapple through
a juice extractor with
2 medium chopped apples
and 1 medium peeled orange.

yogurt
2 x 200g skim-milk
fruit-flavoured yogurt.

SHOPPING LIST

This comprehensive list covers every ingredient in the low-fat diet; most of the staples will already be in your pantry.

STAPLES

1 can cooking-oil spray
Small bottle olive oil
Small bottle sesame oil
Small bottle white wine vinegar
Small bottle red wine vinegar
Small bottle balsamic vinegar
Small bottle white balsamic vinegar
Small bottle sweet chilli sauce
Sea salt flakes
Cracked black pepper
2 x 125g cans chickpeas
2 x 125g cans tuna slices in lemon pepper
185g can tuna in spring water
210g can red salmon
2 x 400g can diced tomatoes
1 small can light coconut milk
425g can baby beetroot
400g can cannellini beans
1 packet pearl barley
1 packet red lentils
1 packet yellow split peas
2 x 1 litre chicken stock
Small packet vegetable stock (you need 180ml)
1 x 250ml fish stock
Small jar baby capers
1 jar dijon mustard
1 jar wholegrain mustard
Small jar horseradish cream
1 bottle reduced-fat mayonnaise
Small bottle oil-free italian dressing
1 small jar tomato chutney
Small packet rolled oats
Small box Weet-Bix
1 packet triticale flakes
1 packet barley flakes
1 packet spelt flakes
1 packet rice flakes
1 packet unprocessed bran
1 jar honey
Small bottle golden syrup
1 packet pepitas

1 packet linseeds
1 packet sunflower seeds
1 packet dried apricots
1 packet dried apple
1 packet dried dates
1 small packet sultanas
Small packet currants
Small packet pine nuts
1 jar curry paste
Small jar tikka masala curry paste
Coriander seeds
Caraway seeds
Dried chilli flakes
Ground fennel
Ground coriander
Ground cumin
Ground cinnamon
Sumac
Hot paprika
Cayenne pepper
Small packet sesame seeds
Small packet caster sugar
Small packet white sugar
Small packet light brown sugar
Small packet palm sugar
Small packet wholemeal self-raising flour
Small packet self-raising flour
Small packet cornflour
Small packet bicarbonate of soda
Small bottle vanilla essence
1 small jar semi-dried tomatoes in oil
Small jar char-grilled eggplant, zucchini and capsicums
Small jar tomato paste
Small bottle teriyaki marinade
Small bottle light soy sauce
Small bottle oyster sauce
Small bottle fish sauce
Small bottle tomato sauce
Small bottle worcestershire sauce
Small packet aborio rice
Small packet brown rice
Small packet polenta

Small packet couscous
100g packet bean thread noodles
Small packet rice stick noodles
Small packet whole wheat penne pasta
Small jar apple sauce

SHOPPING LIST WEEK 1

FRIDGE

500ml skim milk
100g tub low-fat yogurt
100g tub low-fat plain yogurt
12 eggs
75g firm goat's cheese
100g low-fat ricotta

FRUIT & VEGETABLES

250g lychees
100g seedless red grapes
½ small pineapple
½ small honey dew melon
4 medium lemons
5 limes
2 lebanese cucumbers
4 fresh small red thai chillies
1 fresh long red chilli
2 bunches coriander
2 bunches mint
2 bunches flat-leaf parsley
1 bunch chives
1 bunch dill
1 small butter lettuce
1 baby cos lettuce
600g baby spinach leaves
1 iceberg lettuce
20g mixed salad leaves
125g bunch rocket
100g swiss brown mushrooms
150g button mushrooms
50g oyster mushrooms
1 bulb garlic (need 7 cloves)
20g piece ginger
20g lemon grass
1 bunch green onions
1 small carrot

1 medium carrot
1 small zucchini
½ bunch celery
1 small potato
1 large potato
1 small packet snow pea sprouts
1 small avocado
200g beetroot
3 large red radishes
250g cherry tomatoes
250g baby truss egg tomatoes
3 large egg tomatoes
3 medium tomatoes
1 small fennel
1 small red onion
3 small brown onions
3 small red capsicums
1 medium cob corn
50g watercress
120g bean sprouts

MEAT & SEAFOOD

3 chicken breast fillet (450g)
300g lamb fillets
300g piece beef eye fillet
2 boneless pork fillets (300g)
300g pork and veal mince
400g firm white fish fillets
16 uncooked large green prawns (1.1kg)
1kg large black mussels
200g smoked chicken
100g shaved ham

MISCELLANEOUS

1 packet pitta bread
1 packet mini pappadums
1 loaf ciabatta bread
1 loaf soy and linseed bread
1 packet corn tortilla
1 small jar preserved lemons

SHOPPING LIST
WEEK 2

FRIDGE
15 eggs
30g low-fat cheddar cheese
280g low-fat plain yogurt
1 small block parmesan cheese
600ml carton skim milk
260g low-fat ricotta cheese

FRUIT & VEGETABLES
1kg watermelon
750g strawberries
125g blueberries
¼ small rockmelon
¼ small pineapple
1 small mango
1 medium apple
1 small banana
6 medium lemons
1 orange
6 lime
2 bunches mint
2 bunches chives
3 bunches flat-leaf parsley
2 bunches basil
2 bunches coriander
1 small green capsicum
2 lebanese cucumbers
2 small red radishes
250g red grape tomatoes
125g yellow tear drop tomatoes
250g baby trussed tomatoes
1 bunch green onions
3 small brown onions
1 small red onion
1 bulb garlic (need 9 cloves)
10g fresh ginger
170g baby rocket leaves
1 medium tomato
2 fresh long red chillies
2 small fresh red thai chillies
1 fresh long green chilli
4 medium zucchini
1 medium radicchio
100g mixed salad leaves
1 small kumara
1 small carrot
2 medium carrots
100g cauliflower
2 baby eggplant
1 large potato
170g asparagus
50g snow peas
1 small packet snow pea sprouts (need 50g)
1 cob corn
1 small red capsicum
185g baby spinach leaves

250g choy sum
100g button mushrooms

MEAT & SEAFOOD
2 chicken breast fillets (200g)
4 lamb fillets (350g)
250g piece beef eye fillet
400g pork tenderloin
2 x 200g blue-eye cutlets
500g cooked medium prawns
100g sliced ham off the bone
100g light ham
50g smoked shaved turkey

MISCELLANEOUS
1 packet rye mountain bread wraps
125g char-grilled red capsicums in oil
1 loaf wholemeal bread
1 loaf light rye bread
2 white bread rolls
1 loaf ciabatta bread
1 packet pappadums
1 packet wholemeal english muffins

SHOPPING LIST
WEEK 3

FRIDGE
Small tub low-fat margarine
600ml carton skim milk
5 eggs
635g low-fat plain yogurt
175g low-fat fetta cheese
1 small box fillo pastry
1 small block parmesan cheese (should be left over from week 2)
50g bocconcini
600ml carton buttermilk

FRUIT & VEGETABLES
6 limes
4 lemons
375g punnet small strawberries
2 medium stems rhubarb
200g pineapple
150g rockmelon
125g punnet blueberries
2 medium blood oranges
2 medium bananas
5 passionfruit
2 corella pears
1 green mango
600g peeled pumpkin pieces
4 small red onions
1 medium red onion
1 small brown onion
1 large brown onion

2 bunches green onions (need 16 onions)
1 bulb garlic (need 7 cloves)
100g green beans
15g piece fresh ginger
1 small fresh red thai chilli
2 bunches baby buk choy (500g)
1 bunch green onions
80g bean sprouts
3 bunches coriander
2 bunch mint
1 bunch basil
1 bunch thyme
1 bunch dill
1 bunch rosemary
1 bunch marjoram
75g baby spinach leaves
2 medium carrots
125g choy sum
5 lebanese cucumber
200g mixed salad leaves
60g baby mizuna
1 small tomato
5 medium egg tomatoes
150g button mushrooms
2 stalks celery
2 small red capsicums
1 medium red capsicum
680g asparagus
100g curly endive
125g red witlof
130g baby rocket leaves
6 kaffir lime leaves
10g piece lemon grass

MEAT & SEAFOOD
150g chicken breast fillet
3 lamb fillets (200g)
2 x 200g veal chops
250g pork fillets
2 x 200g blue-eye fillets
2 x 200g ocean trout fillets
150g shaved light ham
500g barbecued chicken

MISCELLANEOUS
Small packet smoked almonds
1 packet wholemeal pitta pocket bread
1 small loaf wholemeal bread
1 loaf turkish bread
35g stale wholemeal bread crumbs
2 wholemeal bread rolls
1 x 25cm round pizza base (180g)
50g seeded black olives

SHOPPING LIST
SNACKS

STAPLES
Small jar tomato salsa
1 packet corn thins
1 packet popping corn
1 packet rice thins
1 packet plain rice crackers
1 small jar honey

FRIDGE
200g tub low-fat ricotta cheese
160g tub light chive and onion cream cheese
160g tub light cream cheese
2 x 200g skim milk fruit-flavoured yogurt
600ml carton skim milk
200g tub low-fat cottage cheese
1 small tub low-fat hummus
1 small tub low-fat spicy capsicum dip

FRUIT & VEGETABLES
3 x 250g punnet strawberries
125g punnet blueberries
125g punnet raspberries
250g grapes
250g cherries
2 small bananas
4 medium oranges
2 small pears
5 kiwi fruit
650g watermelon
400g rockmelon
1 medium mandarin
½ small pineapple
2 medium apples
1 small apple
2 small carrots
2 medium carrots
1 avocado
1 small tomato
1 lebanese cucumber
100g sugar snap peas
1 small red capsicum
4 sticks celery
1 medium beetroot

MISCELLANEOUS
1 packet crumpets

GLOSSARY

BARLEY FLAKES barley that has had its hull (hard, outer shells) removed and then flattened.

BEANS
butter also known as lima beans; large, flat, kidney-shaped bean, off-white in colour, with a mealy texture and mild taste. Available canned and dried.
green also known as french or string beans (although the tough string they once had has generally been bred out of them); this long thin fresh bean is consumed in its entirety once cooked.
sprouts also known as bean shoots; tender new growths of assorted beans and seeds.

BEEF EYE FILLET a very tender cut from the area below the rib cage; also known as beef tenderloin.

BICARBONATE OF SODA also known as baking or carb soda; used as a raising agent in baking.

BLOOD ORANGE a virtually seedless citrus fruit with blood-red rind and flesh; it has a sweet, non-acidic pulp and juice.

BRAN, UNPROCESSED made from the outer layer of a cereal, most often the husks of wheat, rice or oats.

BREAD
ciabatta in Italian, the word means slipper, which is the traditional shape of this popular crisp-crusted white bread.
english muffin a round teacake made from yeast, flour, milk, some semolina and salt; often confused with crumpets. Pre-baked and sold packaged in supermarkets; split open and toast before eating.
mountain wraps a soft-textured, thin, flat bread used for sandwiches or rolled up and filled.
pitta also known as lebanese bread; a wheat-flour pocket bread sold in large, flat pieces that separate into two thin rounds. Also available in small thick pieces called pocket pitta.
sourdough has a very lightly sour taste from the yeast starter culture used to make the bread. A low-risen bread with a dense centre and crisp crust.
tortillas thin, round unleavened bread originating in Mexico. Two kinds are available, one made from wheat flour and the other from corn (maize meal).
turkish also known pide. Comes in long (about 45cm) flat loaves as well as individual rounds.

BUTTERMILK originally the term given to the slightly sour liquid left after butter was churned from cream, today it is made similarly to yogurt. Sold alongside fresh milk products in supermarkets; despite the implication of its name, it's low in fat.

CAPSICUM also known as bell pepper or, simply, pepper. Membranes and seeds should be discarded before use.

CAYENNE PEPPER long, thin-fleshed, extremely hot red chilli that is usually sold dried and ground.

CHEESE
bocconcini meaning 'mouthful', is the term used for walnut-sized, baby mozzarella; a delicate, semi-soft, white cheese. Spoils rapidly so keep under refrigeration, in brine, for 1 or 2 days.
cheddar the most widely eaten cheese in the world, cheddar is a semi-hard cow's-milk cheese. It ranges in colour from white to pale yellow, and has a slightly crumbly texture if properly matured. It's aged for between nine months and two years, and the flavour becomes sharper with time.
fetta a crumbly goat's- or sheep-milk cheese with a sharp salty taste.
goat's made from goat's milk; has an earthy, strong taste. Available in soft and firm textures, in various shapes and sizes, sometimes rolled in ash or herbs.
parmesan a hard, grainy cow's-milk cheese. The curd is salted in brine for a month before being aged for up to two years in humid conditions.
ricotta soft, white cheese made from whey, a by-product of other cheese-making, to which fresh milk and acid are added. Ricotta is a sweet, moist cheese with a slightly grainy texture.

CHICKEN
breast fillet is skinned and boned.
smoked ready-to-eat, available as a whole small bird or breasts; sold cryovac-packed in supermarkets.

CHILLI
flakes crushed dried chillies.
green any unripened chilli; also some varieties that are ripe when green, such as jalapeño, habanero or serrano.
long available both fresh and dried and as red or green; a generic term used for any moderately hot, long (about 6cm to 8cm), thin chilli.
red thai also known as 'scuds'; small, very hot and bright red; substitute with fresh serrano or habanero chillies.

CINNAMON dried inner bark of the shoots of the cinnamon tree; available in stick (quill) or ground form.

CORELLA PEARS miniature dessert pears up to 10cm long.

CORIANDER also known as pak chee, cilantro or chinese parsley; bright-green leafy herb with a pungent flavour. Both the stems and roots of coriander are used in cooking; wash well before using. Also available ground or as seeds; these should not be substituted for fresh coriander as the tastes are completely different.

CORNFLOUR (cornstarch) used as a thickening agent. Available as wheaten and 100% maize (corn) cornflour.

COUSCOUS a fine, grain-like cereal product made from semolina; a dough of semolina flour and water is sieved then dehydrated to produce minuscule even-sized pellets of couscous. It is rehydrated by steaming, or with the addition of a warm liquid, and swells to three or four times its original size.

CUMIN, GROUND a spice also known as zeera or comino.

CURLY ENDIVE see lettuce.

EGGS some recipes in this book may call for raw or barely cooked eggs; exercise caution if there is a salmonella problem in your area. The risk is greater for those who are pregnant, elderly or very young, and those with impaired immune systems.

ENGLISH MUFFIN see bread.

FILLO PASTRY (also filo and phyllo); tissue-thin pastry sheets that are purchased chilled or frozen.

FISH
blue-eye also known as deep sea trevalla or trevally and blue-eye cod; a thick, moist, white-fleshed fish.
firm white fillets blue eye, bream, flathead, swordfish, ling, whiting, jewfish, snapper or sea perch are all good choices. Check for any small pieces of bone in the fillets and use tweezers to remove them.
ocean trout a farmed fish with pink, soft flesh. Atlantic salmon (which is from the same family) can be substituted.

FLOUR
self-raising (rising) plain or wholemeal flour sifted with baking powder in the proportion of 1 cup plain (all-purpose) flour to 2 teaspoons baking powder.

GINGER, FRESH also known as green or root ginger; the thick root of a tropical plant. Trim, removing any creases and knobbly pieces, then grate or slice thinly.

GOLDEN SYRUP a by-product of refined sugar cane; pure maple syrup or honey can be substituted.

GREEN MANGO sour and crunchy, green mangoes are just immature fruit. They will keep, wrapped in plastic, in the fridge for up to two weeks.

HORSERADISH CREAM commercially prepared creamy paste made of grated horseradish, vinegar, oil and sugar.

KAFFIR LIME LEAF also known as bai magrood, sold fresh, dried or frozen. Looks like two glossy dark green leaves joined end to end, forming a rounded hourglass shape. Dried leaves are less potent, so double the number called for in a recipe if you substitute them for fresh leaves. A strip of fresh lime peel may be substituted for each kaffir lime leaf.

LAMB FILLETS also known as lamb tenderloin; from the loin (lower back) section. Lamb backstrap may be substituted, although this cut is larger than the fillet.

LETTUCE
butter have small, round, loosely formed heads with soft, buttery-textured leaves ranging from pale green on the outer leaves to pale yellow-green on the inner leaves. Has a sweet flavour.
cos, baby red these miniature red lettuces have firm dimpled leaves with deep burgundy tips and a bright green central vein. Most major supermarkets stock this new breed of lettuce.
curly endive also known as frisée, a curly-leafed green vegetable.
iceberg a heavy, firm round lettuce with tightly packed crisp leaves.
mizuna leaves Japanese in origin, a frizzy green salad leaf with a delicate mustard flavour.
oakleaf also known as Feuille de Chene. Available in both red and green leaf. Tender and mildly-flavoured with curly, floppy leaves.
radicchio Italian in origin; a member of the chicory family. The dark burgundy leaves have a strong, bitter flavour; they can be cooked or eaten raw in salads.
witlof cigar-shaped, tightly packed heads with pale, yellow-green tips. Has a delicately bitter flavour.

LINSEEDS also known as flaxseed; from the seeds of the flax plant.

MIZUNA LEAVES see lettuce.

MUSTARD, WHOLEGRAIN is also known as seeded mustard. A french-style coarse-grain mustard made from crushed mustard seeds and dijon-style french mustard.

NUTMEG dried nut of an evergreen tree native to Indonesia; available ground or whole (grate your own with a fine grater).

OIL
cooking spray we use a cholesterol-free spray made from canola oil.
macadamia extracted from crushed macadamia nuts.
olive made from ripened olives. Extra virgin and virgin are the best, while extra light or light refers to taste, not fat levels.
peanut pressed from ground peanuts; most commonly used oil in Asian cooking because of its high smoke point (can handle high heat without burning).
sesame made from roasted, crushed, white sesame seeds; a flavouring rather than a cooking medium.
vegetable sourced from plants rather than animal fats.

ONION
brown and white are interchangeable, however, white onions have a more pungent flesh.
green an immature onion picked before the bulb has formed, having a long, bright-green edible stalk. Also known as scallion or, incorrectly, shallot.
red also known as spanish, red spanish or bermuda onion; sweet-flavoured, large, purple-red onion.
spring have small white bulbs and long narrow green-leafed tops.

PAPPADUMS dried wafers made from a combination of lentil and rice flours, oil and spices.

PAPRIKA GROUND, dried, sweet red capsicum (bell pepper); there are many grades and types available, including sweet, hot, mild and smoked.

PEPPERCORNS, DRIED GREEN soft, unripe berry of the pepper plant, usually sold packed in brine (occasionally found dried, packed in salt). Has a distinctive fresh taste.

PINE NUTS also known as pignoli; not actually a nut, it's a small, cream-coloured kernel from pine cones.

PIZZA BASES pre-packaged bases for home-made pizzas. Available in various sizes (snack or family), and thicknesses (thin and crispy, or thick).

POLENTA also known as cornmeal; a flour-like cereal made of ground corn (maize). Is also the name of the dish that is made from it.

PORK
fillets (tenderloin) comes from the full pork loin. As the name indicates, the tenderloin is one of the most tender cuts of pork.
steaks, boneless from the loin, which runs along most of the back.
tenderloin see fillet.

RED RADISH peppery root vegetable related to the mustard plant. The small round red variety is the mildest; it is crisp and juicy, and eaten raw in salads.

RHUBARB has thick, celery-like stalks that can reach up to 60cm long (choose fresh crisp stalks); the stalks are the only edible portion of the plant – the leaves contain a toxic substance. Although rhubarb is generally eaten as a fruit, it is a vegetable.

RICE
arborio originated from the town of Arborio in Italy. This small, round-grained rice is suited to absorb a large amount of liquid; when cooked, the grain becomes firm, creamy and chewy in texture.
brown retains the outer bran layer of the rice grain. When cooked, it has a slightly chewy texture and a nut-like flavour.
jasmine a fragrant, long-grained rice; white rice can be substituted, but will not taste the same.

RICE FLAKES husked rice that has been flattened into light, dry flakes that swell when added to liquid. The thicknesses of these flakes vary between almost translucently thin (the more expensive varieties) to nearly four times thicker than a normal rice grain.

ROLLED OATS oat groats (which are oats that have been husked) that have been steamed-softened, flattened with rollers, dried and then packaged for consumption as a cereal product.

SAMBAL OELEK (also ulek or olek) Indonesian in origin, this salty paste is made from ground chillies and vinegar. It is used to add heat to dishes without altering the other flavours.

SAUCE

fish called naam pla on the label if it is Thai made; the Vietnamese version, nuoc naam, is almost identical. Made from pulverised salted fermented fish (most often anchovies); has a pungent smell and a strong taste. There are many versions of varying intensity, so use according to your taste.

oyster Asian in origin, this rich, brown sauce is made from oysters and their brine, cooked with salt and soy sauce, and thickened with starches.

soy made from fermented soya beans. Several variations are available in most supermarkets and Asian food stores. We use a mild Japanese-style variety in our recipes; possibly the best table soy and the one to choose if you only want to use one variety.

light soy fairly thin in consistency and, while paler than the others, is the saltiest tasting; used in dishes in which the natural colour of the ingredients is to be maintained. Not to be confused with salt-reduced or low-sodium soy sauces.

sweet chilli a mild, Thai-style sauce made from red chillies, sugar, garlic and vinegar.

tomato also known as ketchup or catsup; a flavoured condiment made from tomatoes, vinegar and spices.

worcestershire this dark brown spicy condiment is made from garlic, soy sauce, tamarind, onions, molasses, lime, anchovies, vinegar and other seasonings. It is available in most supermarkets.

SCALLOPS
a bivalve mollusc with a fluted shell valve; we use scallops that have the coral (roe) removed. Available on the half-shell or shelled.

SKIM MILK
has less than or equal to 0.15 per cent fat. Sometimes milk solids are added to optimise the taste.

SNOW PEAS
also mange tout ('eat all'). *Snow pea tendrils*, the growing shoots of the plant, are sold by greengrocers. *Snow pea sprouts* are the tender new growths of snow peas, and are also known as mange tout.

STOCK
tetra packs, cans, bottles, cubes, powder or concentrated liquid can be used. As a guide, 1 teaspoon of stock powder or 1 small crumbled stock cube or 1 portion stock concentrate mixed with 1 cup water will give a fairly strong stock. Be aware of the salt and fat content of stocks.

SUGAR

brown a finely granulated, extremely soft, sugar retaining molasses for its characteristic colour and flavour.

caster also known as superfine or finely granulated table sugar.

palm also known as nam tan pip, jaggery, jawa or gula melaka; made from the sap of the sugar palm tree. Light brown to black in colour and usually sold in rock-hard cakes; the sugar of choice in Indian and most South-East Asian cooking. If palm sugar is unavailable, substitute it with brown sugar, instead.

white a coarse, granulated table sugar, also known as crystal sugar.

SULTANAS
dried grapes, also known as golden raisins.

SUNFLOWER KERNELS
dried husked sunflower seeds. Available from health-food stores and most supermarkets.

TERIYAKI MARINADE
a blend of soy sauce, wine, vinegar and spices.

TIKKA MASALA CURRY PASTE
is a mild aromatic, slightly smoky, rich curry based on tomatoes and cream or coconut cream.

TOMATO

cherry also known as tiny tim or tom thumb tomatoes, small and round.

egg also called plum or roma; these are the smallish, oval-shaped tomatoes much used in Italian cooking.

grape are about the size of a grape; they can be oblong, pear or grape-shaped and are often used whole in salads or eaten as a snack.

paste triple-concentrated tomato puree that's used to flavour soups, stews, sauces and casseroles.

semi-dried partially dried tomato pieces in olive oil; softer and juicier than sun-dried, these are not a preserve so do not keep as long as sun-dried tomatoes.

sun-dried we use sun-dried tomatoes packaged in oil, unless otherwise specified; drain well before using.

TRITICALE FLAKES
made from the triticale grain (a cross between wheat and rye). Grains of triticale are rolled and flattened into flakes.

VANILLA EXTRACT
is made by extracting the flavour from the vanilla bean pod; the pods are usually soaked in alcohol, which captures the authentic vanilla flavour.

vanilla extract made by pulping chopped vanilla beans with a mixture of alcohol and water. This gives a very strong solution, and only a couple of drops are needed to flavour most dishes.

VEAL

chops, loin cut from the backbone.

cutlets a choice chop cut from the mid-loin (back) area.

T-bone T-shaped bone in and fillet eye attached.

schnitzel thinly sliced steak available crumbed or plain; we used plain schnitzel in our recipes.

VINEGAR

balsamic made from the juice of trebbiano grapes; it is a deep rich brown colour with a sweet and sour flavour. Originally from Modena, Italy, there are now many balsamic vinegars on the market ranging in pungency and quality, depending on how long they have been aged. Quality can be determined up to a point by price; use the most expensive sparingly.

white balsamic (also known as balsamic white condiment or dressing) this is a clear, lighter version of balsamic vinegar, having a fresh, sweet clean taste.

brown malt made from fermented malt and beech shavings.

cider (apple cider) made from crushed fermented apples.

red wine based on a blend of fermented red wine.

white wine made from a blend of white wines.

WEET-BIX
oven-roasted whole wheat grains and barley malt extract – it is a wheat-based breakfast biscuit.

WHEAT GERM
is the embryo from which the seed germinates to form the sprout that becomes wheat. The term 'germ' comes from the word germinate. It has a nutty flavour and is very oily, which causes it to turn rancid quickly. Wheat germ is usually separated from the bran and starch during the milling of flour because the germ's perishable oil content limits the keeping time of the flour. It is available from health-food stores and supermarkets.

WITLOF
see lettuce.

YOGURT, LOW-FAT
we used yogurt with a fat content of less than 0.2%.

INDEX

Published in 2013 by ACP Books, Sydney
ACP Books are published by ACP Magazines Limited
a division of Nine Entertainment Co.
54 Park St, Sydney
GPO Box 4088, Sydney, NSW 2001.
phone (02) 9282 8618; fax (02) 9126 3702
acpbooks@acpmagazines.com.au; www.acpbooks.com.au

ACP BOOKS
Publishing Director, ACP Magazines - Gerry Reynolds
Publisher - Sally Wright
Editorial and Food Director - Pamela Clark
Creative Director - Hieu Chi Nguyen

Published and Distributed in the United Kingdom by Octopus Publishing Group
Endeavour House
189 Shaftesbury Avenue
London WC2H 8JY
United Kingdom
phone (+44)(0)207 632 5400; fax (+44)(0)207 632 5405
info@octopus-publishing.co.uk;
www.octopusbooks.co.uk

Printed by Toppan Printing Co., China

International foreign language rights, Brian Cearnes, ACP Books bcearnes@acpmagazines.com.au

A catalogue record for this book is available from the British Library.
ISBN: 978-1-907428-83-8 (pbk.)
© ACP Magazines Ltd 2013
ABN 18 053 273 546

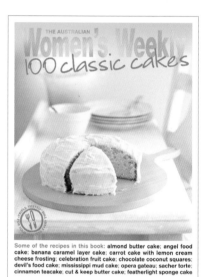

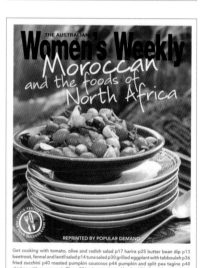